The Complete Guide to **Chain**

TSUBAKI

The Complete Guide to Chain
© 1997 by U.S. Tsubaki, Inc.

First English-language edition, 1997
ISBN 0-9658932-0-0
Library of Congress 97-061464

Translated and printed with permission
of Kogyo Chosakai Publishing Co., Ltd.
Distributed in North America, Australia, and Europe
by U.S. Tsubaki, Inc., 301 East Marquardt Drive,
Wheeling, Illinois 60090. Originally published by
Kogyo Chosakai Publishing Co., Ltd., under the title:
Machine Elements Manual, Chain.

Original Editor: Tsubakimoto Chain Co.
Original Publisher: Sachio Shimura

Contributors

Supervising Editor
Kyosuke Otoshi
Director
Chain Products Division

Editor
Makoto Kanehira
Manager
Chain Products Division
Production Engineering Department

Writers
Makoto Kanehira
Manager
Chain Products Division
Production Engineering Department

Tomofumi Otani
Manager
Chain Products Division
Engineering Department
Chain Engineering Section

Masayuki Yoshikawa
Manager
Chain Products Division
Engineering Department
Conveyor Chain Engineering Section

Toshio Takahashi
Manager
Chain Products Division
Roller Chain Production Department
Engineering Plastics Manufacturing Section

Contents

BASICS SECTION

APPLICATIONS SECTION

6. LARGE PITCH CONVEYOR CHAINS

COFFEE BREAKS

Preface

When most people hear the word "chain," they imagine a short-link chain, which consists of connected metal rings, or the type of chain used on a motorcycle or bicycle. However, chains of every size and description are used in factories, even though they are rarely seen in daily life. In fact, most people probably don't notice that chain is being used all around them, in parking elevators or escalators, for example.

Steel roller chain, which is the ultimate in chain design, and constitutes the majority of chain produced today, is a relatively new invention. Its history is only about 100 years old. It is newer as a machine part than gears and belts. In Japan, the first chain was imported with bicycles during the Meiji-period (1867~1912 A.D.). Domestic production started when the supply from the United States and European countries was stopped during World War I.

There are two functions of chain: power transmission and conveyance. For transmission roller chains, Japanese chain makers gradually changed the priority of production from bicycle chain to industrial chain. After World War II, these chains challenged the advanced chain from the United States and Europe. Now they have achieved the highest levels in the world for both quality and quantity. This holds true for conveyor chain, as well.

The industries that are the main users of the chain, including automobile, electronics, steel, chemical, environmental, food, bicycle, and motorcycle industries, have developed new technologies and production methods that require various high performance chain. These industries are looking for improvement in tensile strength, fatigue strength, abrasion resistance, environmental resistance, and efficiency, as well as perfection of maintenance-free chain products. To satisfy these many requirements, chain makers are making every effort to improve chain's basic performance step by step. In addition, new chain technologies, including rolling bearing systems, super engineered plastic, and free flow chains, are being developed. Because of these two factors, chains with special characteristics are now being produced.

During his lifetime of experience, the editor of this book has helped to develop most of these new types of chain. He has also acquired a great deal of practical knowledge through his contacts with end users. Accordingly, this comprehensive book explains the points that readers may want to know, including the most important point: determining the quality of the chain. I hope this book can always be with you when you use chains.

I'm afraid some of the descriptions in this book may be either inadequate or hard to understand; therefore, I hope that readers will point out any mistakes and send me their comments and input. Furthermore, because this book is

based on a lot of technical data and specialized books, I would like to extend
many thanks to them all. I also thank Mr. Seihin Shibuya, vice-director of
Kogyo Chosakai Publishing Co., Ltd., for his whole-hearted efforts in publishing this book.

March 1995

Kyosuke Otoshi
Director, Chain Products Division
Tsubakimoto Chain Co.

Acknowledgments

The following people contributed considerable time, talent, and energy to ensure the accurate translation and timely publication of *The Complete Guide to Chain*.

David Doray
Director
Corporate Marketing Department
U.S. Tsubaki, Inc.

Lee Marcus
Marketing Communications Specialist
Corporate Marketing Department
U.S. Tsubaki, Inc.

James Lamoureux
Design & Application Engineer
Product Engineering
Roller Chain Division
U.S. Tsubaki, Inc.

Mokoto Kameda
Project Administrator
Customer Service and Materials
Roller Chain Division
U.S. Tsubaki, Inc.

Katsuya Matsuda
Coordinator
Strategic Business Development
  Department
U.S. Tsubaki, Inc.

Toshiharu Yamamoto
Quality Manager
Product Engineering
Roller Chain Division
U.S. Tsubaki, Inc.

Jack Kane
Manager
Customer Service and Materials
Roller Chain Division
U.S. Tsubaki, Inc.

Leszek Wawer
Senior Design & Application Engineer
Product Engineering
Atlanta Service Center
U.S. Tsubaki, Inc.

Editorial services provided by
  Drake Creative, Inc., Chicago, IL

Design services provided by
  Toomey Associates, Ltd., Hinsdale, IL

1. CHAIN BASICS

1.1 WHAT IS A CHAIN?

A chain is a reliable machine component, which transmits power by means of tensile forces, and is used primarily for power transmission and conveyance systems. The function and uses of chain are similar to a belt. There are many kinds of chain. It is convenient to sort types of chain by either material of composition or method of construction.

We can sort chains into five types:
1. Cast iron chain.
2. Cast steel chain.
3. Forged chain.
4. Steel chain.
5. Plastic chain.

Demand for the first three chain types is now decreasing; they are only used in some special situations. For example, cast iron chain is part of water-treatment equipment; forged chain is used in overhead conveyors for automobile factories.

In this book, we are going to focus on the latter two: "steel chain," especially the type called "roller chain," which makes up the largest share of chains being produced, and "plastic chain."

For the most part, we will refer to "roller chain" simply as "chain."

> NOTE: Roller chain is a chain that has an inner plate, outer plate, pin, bushing, and roller.

In the following section of this book, we will sort chains according to their uses, which can be broadly divided into six types:
1. Power transmission chain.
2. Small pitch conveyor chain.
3. Precision conveyor chain.
4. Top chain.
5. Free flow chain.
6. Large pitch conveyor chain.

The first one is used for power transmission, the other five are used for conveyance. In the Applications Section of this book, we will describe the uses and features of each chain type by following the above classification.

In the following section, we will explain the composition of power transmission chain, small pitch chain, and large pitch conveyor chain. Because there are special features in the composition of precision conveyor chain, top chain, and free flow chain, check the appropriate pages in the Applications Section about these features.

1.1.1 Basic Structure of Power Transmission Chain

A typical configuration for RS60-type chain is shown in Figure 1.1.

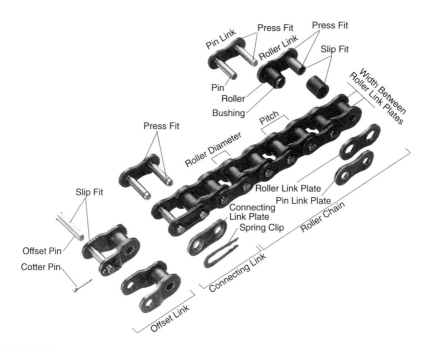

Figure 1.1 The Basic Components of Transmission Chain

Connecting Link

This is the ordinary type of connecting link. The pin and link plate are slip fit in the connecting link for ease of assembly. This type of connecting link is 20 percent lower in fatigue strength than the chain itself. There are also some special connecting links which have the same strength as the chain itself. (See Figure 1.2.)

Tap Fit Connecting Link

In this link, the pin and the tap fit connecting link plate are press fit. It has fatigue strength almost equal to that of the chain itself. (See Figure 1.2.)

Offset Link

An offset link is used when an odd number of chain links is required. It is 35 percent lower in fatigue strength than the chain itself. The pin and two plates are slip fit. There is also a two-pitch offset link available that has a fatigue strength as great as the chain itself. (See Figure 1.3.)

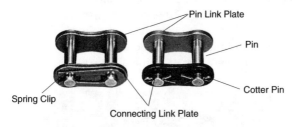

Pin Link Plate

Pin

Cotter Pin

Spring Clip

Connecting Link Plate

Spring Clip Connecting Link   **Cotter Connecting Link**

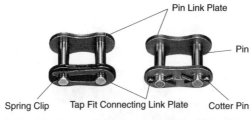

Pin Link Plate

Pin

Cotter Pin

Spring Clip   Tap Fit Connecting Link Plate

Spring Clip Connecting Link   **Cotter Connecting Link**

Figure 1.2   Standard Connecting Link (top) and Tap Fit Connecting Link (bottom)

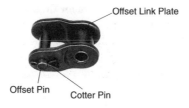

Offset Link Plate

Offset Pin   Cotter Pin

Figure 1.3   Offset Link

1.1.2 Basic Structure of Small Pitch Conveyor Chain

The basic structure is the same as that of power transmission chain. Figure 1.4 shows a single pitch conveyor chain. The double pitch type in Figure 1.5 has an outer plate and an inner plate of the same height, but often has a roller with a larger diameter. Usually, an attachment is used with this chain.

Figure 1.4   Single Pitch Conveyor Chain with K-1 Attachment

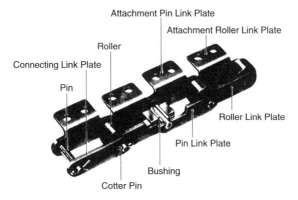

Figure 1.5   Basic Structure of Double Pitch Conveyor Chain with A-2 Attachment

1.1.3 Basic Structure of Large Pitch Conveyor Chain—Engineering Class

Large pitch conveyor chain has the same basic structure as double pitch conveyor chain (Figure 1.5), but there are some differences. Large pitch conveyor chain (Figure 1.6) has a headed pin, sometimes a flanged roller (F-roller), and usually does not use a riveted pin. Large pitch conveyor chain is also called engineering class chain.

1.1.4 Functions of Chain Parts

Plate

The plate is the component that bears the tension placed on the chain. Usually this is a repeated loading, sometimes accompanied by shock. Therefore, the plate must have not only great static tensile strength, but also must hold up to the dynamic forces of load and shock. Furthermore, the plate must meet environmental resistance requirements (for example, corrosion, abrasion, etc.).

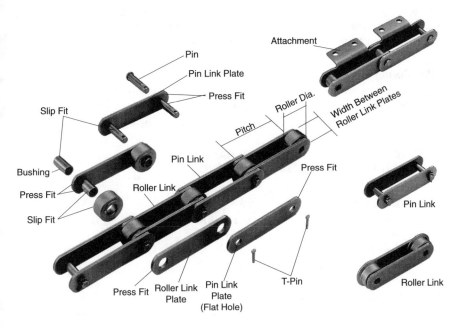

Attachment

Pin

Pin Link Plate

Press Fit

Slip Fit

Roller Dia.

Width Between Roller Link Plates

Pitch

Bushing

Press Fit

Pin Link

Press Fit

Pin Link

Slip Fit

Roller Link

Pin Link

T-Pin

Roller Link

Press Fit   **Roller Link Plate**   **Pin Link Plate (Flat Hole)**

Figure 1.6   Basic Structure of Large Pitch Conveyor Chain

Pin

The pin is subject to shearing and bending forces transmitted by the plate. At the same time, it forms a load-bearing part, together with the bushing, when the chain flexes during sprocket engagement. Therefore, the pin needs high tensile and shear strength, resistance to bending, and also must have sufficient endurance against shock and wear.

Bushing

The bushing is subject to shearing and bending stresses transmitted by the plate and roller, and also gets shock loads when the chain engages the sprocket.

In addition, when the chain articulates, the inner surface forms a load-bearing part together with the pin. The outer surface also forms a load-bearing part with the roller's inner surface when the roller rotates on the rail or engages the sprocket. Therefore, it must have great tensile strength against shearing and be resistant to dynamic shock and wear.

Roller

The roller is subject to impact load as it strikes the sprocket teeth during the chain engagement with the sprocket. After engagement, the roller changes its point of contact and balance. It is held between the sprocket teeth and bushing, and moves on the tooth face while receiving a compression load.

Furthermore, the roller's inner surface constitutes a bearing part together with the bushing's outer surface when the roller rotates on the rail. Therefore, it must be resistant to wear and still have strength against shock, fatigue, and compression.

Cotter Pin, Spring Clip, T-Pin

These are the parts that prevent the outer plate from falling off the pin at the point of connection. They may wear out during high-speed operation, therefore, for this application, these parts require heat treatment.

1.2 ADVANTAGES AND DISADVANTAGES OF CHAIN FOR POWER TRANSMISSION AND CONVEYORS

1.2.1 Power Transmission Uses

Power transmission machines use either chains, gears, or belts. Table 1.1 provides a comparison of typical applications.

Usually, chain is an economical part of power transmission machines for low speeds and large loads. However, it is also possible to use chain in high-speed conditions like automobile engine camshaft drives. This is accomplished by devising a method of operation and lubrication.

Basically, there are lower limits of fatigue strength in the gear and the chain, but not in the belt. Furthermore, if a gear tooth breaks, the gear will stop at the next tooth. Therefore, the order is gear > chain > belt in the aspect of reliability.

In most cases:

(1) An increase in gear noise indicates that the end of the service life is near.

(2) You will know that the chain is almost at the end of its life by wear elongation or an increase in vibration caused by wear elongation.

(3) It is difficult to detect toothed-belt life without stopping the machine and inspecting the belt carefully.

It is possible to decrease gear noise by adjusting the gears precisely or by adapting the drive to a helical or double helical gear. Both of these are expensive, and thrust load may occur with the use of helical gears.

Chain is more suitable to long-term continuous running and power transmission with limited torque fluctuation. Gears are more fit to reversing or intermittent drives.

The greater the shaft center distance, the more practical the use of chain and belt, rather than gears.

Table 1.1 Comparison Table

Type		Roller Chain	Tooth Belt	V Belt	Spur Gear
Sychronization		◎	◎	✕	◎
Transmission Efficiency		◎	◎	△	◎
Anti-Shock		△	○	◎	✕
Noise/Vibration		△	○	◎	✕
Surrounding Condition		Avoid Water, Dust	Avoid Heat, Oil, Water, Dust	Avoid Heat, Oil, Water, Dust	Avoid Water, Dust
Space Saving	High Speed Low Load	✕	◎	○	○
	Low Speed High Load	◎ Compact	△ Heavy Pulley	✕ Wider Pulley	○ Less Durability Due to Less Engagement
Lubrication		✕ Required	◎ No Lube	◎ No Lube	✕ Required
Layout Flexibilty		◎	○	△	✕
Excess Load onto Bearing		◎	△	✕	◎

◎ Excellent   ○ Good   △ Fair   ✕ Poor

Generally, under the same transmission conditions, the cost of toothed belts and pulleys is much higher than the cost of chains and sprockets.

See the following features and points of notice about roller chain transmission.

Features of Chain Drives:

1. Speed reduction/increase of up to seven to one can be easily accommodated.
2. Chain can accommodate long shaft-center distances (less than 4 m), and is more versatile.
3. It is possible to use chain with multiple shafts or drives with both sides of the chain.
4. Standardization of chains under the American National Standards Institute (ANSI), the International Standardization Organization (ISO), and the Japanese Industrial Standards (JIS) allow ease of selection.
5. It is easy to cut and connect chains.
6. The sprocket diameter for a chain system may be smaller than a belt pulley, while transmitting the same torque.
7. Sprockets are subject to less wear than gears because sprockets distribute the loading over their many teeth.

Points of Notice:

1. Chain has a speed variation, called chordal action, which is caused by the polygonal effect of the sprockets.
2. Chain needs lubrication.
3. Chain wears and elongates.
4. Chain is weak when subjected to loads from the side. It needs proper alignment.

1.2.2 Conveyance Uses

Conveyor systems use either chains, belts, or rollers, depending on the application. The general guidelines for suitability are shown in Table 1.2, and discussed in Basics Section 1.2.1.

Belt conveyors are most suitable for large-volume movement of bulk materials. Except for this situation, chains, belts, and rollers are generally difficult to compare in terms of capacity, speed, or distance of conveyance of unit materials.

NOTE: In this discussion, bulk materials refer to items like grain or cement that may shift during conveyance. Unit materials, such as automobiles or cardboard, are stable when conveyed.

Table 1.2

Conveyor Type	Chain	Belt	Roller
Bulk Handling	◎	◎	✕
Unit Handling	◎	○ Only for light conveyor	◎
Dust in Conveying Bulky Goods	◎	✕/○ (○ for closed conveyor)	——
Space Required	Small	Large	Large

◎ Excellent   ○ Good   ✕ Poor

1.3 SPROCKETS

The chain converts rotational power to pulling power, or pulling power to rotational power, by engaging with the sprocket.

The sprocket looks like a gear but differs in three important ways:

1. Sprockets have many engaging teeth; gears usually have only one or two.
2. The teeth of a gear touch and slip against each other; there is basically no slippage in a sprocket.
3. The shape of the teeth are different in gears and sprockets.

Figure 1.7   Types of Sprockets

2. CHAIN DYNAMICS

A study of phenomena that occur during chain use.

2.1 CHAINS UNDER TENSION

A chain can transmit tension, but usually cannot transmit pushing forces. There are actually a few special chains that can push, but this discussion focuses on tension. In the following section we will explain how the chain acts under tension.

2.1.1 Elastic Stretch, Plastic Deformation, and Breakage

Tensile Strength

How will the chain behave when it is subjected to tensile loading? There is a standardized test to determine the tensile strength of a chain. Here's how it works: The manufacturer takes a new, five-link-or-longer power transmission chain and firmly affixes both ends to the jigs (Figure 2.1). Now a load or tension is applied and measurements are taken until the chain breaks (JIS B 1801-1990).

Chain Elongation

As a chain is subjected to increasing stress or load, it becomes longer. This relationship can be graphed (Figure 2.2). The vertical axis shows increasing stress or load, and the horizontal axis shows increasing strain or elongation. In this stress-strain graph, each point represents the following:

O-A: elastic region
A: limit of proportionality for chains; there is not an
   obvious declining point, as in mild steel
A-C: plastic deformation
B: maximum tension point
C: actual breakage

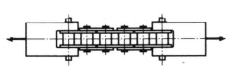

Figure 2.1   Typical Chain in Tensile Test

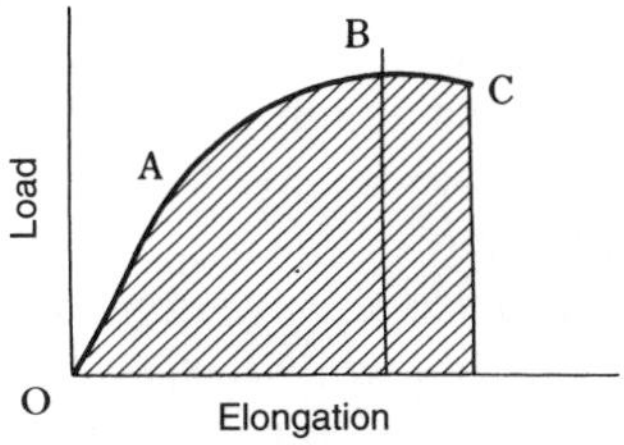

Figure 2.2   Stress-Strain Graph

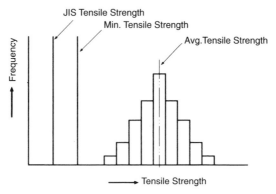

Tensile Strength

Reporting Tensile Strength

Point B, shown in Figure 2.2, the maximum tension point, is also called the *ultimate tensile strength*. In some cases, point B will come at the same time as point C. After breaking a number of chains, a tensile strength graph shows a normal distribution (Figure 2.3).

The average load in Figure 2.3 is called the *average tensile strength,* and the lowest value, which is determined after statistically examining the results, is called the *minimum tensile strength.* JIS (Japanese Industrial Standard) also regulates minimum tensile strength, but it is much lower than any manufacturer's tensile strength listed in their catalogs.

"Maximum allowable load," shown in some manufacturer's catalogs, is based on the fatigue limit (see Basics Section 2.2.2). This value is much lower than point A. Furthermore, in the case of power transmission chain, point A is usually 70 percent of the *ultimate tensile strength* (point B). If the chain receives greater tension than point A, plastic deformation will occur, and the chain will be nonfunctional.

Using Tensile Strength Information

For the sake of safety, you should never subject chains to tension greater than half the *average tensile strength*—not even once. If the chain is inadvertently loaded that high, you should change the whole chain set. If the chain is repeatedly subjected to loads greater than the maximum allowable load, fatigue failure may result.

When you see tensile strength graphs or stress-strain graphs, you should be aware of the following facts:

1. Every manufacturer shows the *average tensile strength* in its catalog, but it is not unusual to find that the value listed may have been developed with sales in mind. Therefore, when comparing chains from different manufacturers, check the *minimum tensile strength.*

2. In addition to the tensile strength, the most important fact about a stress-strain graph is the value of stretch at the time of breakage. If the chain's tensile strength is higher and the capacity to stretch is greater, the chain can absorb more energy before it breaks. This means the chain won't be easily broken even if it receives unexpected shock load. (In Figure 2.2, the cross-hatched area is the value of energy that the chain can absorb before it breaks.)

Elastic Elongation

Another important characteristic in practice is how much elastic elongation the chain will undergo when it is subjected to tension. When you use chains for elevators on stage, if there is a difference between the stage floor and the elevator platform, the dancers will trip on it. In an elevator parking garage, it is necessary to lower cars down to the entrance within a small difference in the level. Therefore, it is important to anticipate how long the chain's elastic stretch will be. Figure 2.4 shows elasticity/stretch for power transmission roller chains.

Please contact the individual manufacturers about small and large pitch conveyor chains.

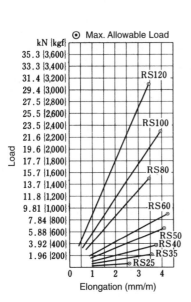
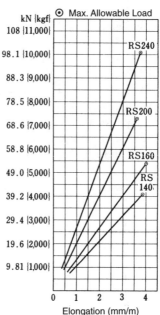

Figure 2.4   Elastic Elongation on Roller Chain

2.1.2 Engagement with Sprockets

Although chains are sometimes pushed and pulled at either end by cylinders, chains are usually driven by wrapping them on sprockets. In the following section, we explain the relation between sprockets and chains when power is transmitted by sprockets.

1. Back tension

First, let us explain the relationship between flat belts and pulleys. Figure 2.5 shows a rendition of a flat belt drive. The circle at the top is a pulley, and the belt hangs down from each side. When the pulley is fixed and the left side of the belt is loaded with tension (T_0), the force needed to pull the belt down to the right side will be:

$$T_1 = T_0 \times e^{\mu\theta}$$

For example, T_0 = 100 N: the coefficient of friction between the belt and pulley, μ = 0.3; the wrap angle θ = π (180°).

$$T_1 = T_0 \times 2.566 = 256.6 \text{ N}$$

In brief, when you use a flat belt in this situation, you can get 256.6 N of drive power only when there is 100 N of back tension. For elements without teeth such as flat belts or ropes, the way to get more drive power is to increase the coefficient of friction or wrapping angle. If a substance, like grease or oil, which decreases the coefficient of friction, gets onto the contact surface, the belt cannot deliver the required tension.

In the chain's case, sprocket teeth hold the chain roller. If the sprocket tooth configuration is square, as in Figure 2.6, the direction of the tooth's reactive force is opposite the chain's tension, and only one tooth will receive all the chain's tension. Therefore, the chain will work without back tension.

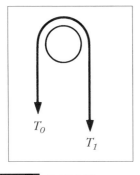

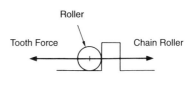

 Figure 2.5　Flat Belt Drive

Figure 2.6　Simplified Roller/Tooth Forces

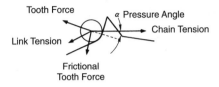

Figure 2.7   The Balance of Forces Around the Roller

But actually, sprocket teeth need some inclination so that the teeth can engage and slip off of the roller. The balance of forces that exist around the roller are shown in Figure 2.7, and it is easy to calculate the required back tension.

For example, assume a coefficient of friction $\mu = 0$, and you can calculate the back tension (T_k) that is needed at sprocket tooth number k with this formula:

$$T_k = T_0 \times \left\{ \frac{\sin \varnothing}{\sin(\varnothing + 2\beta)} \right\}^{k-1}$$

Where:
- T_k = back tension at tooth k
- T_0 = chain tension
- $\varnothing$ = sprocket minimum pressure angle $17 - 64/N(°)$
- N = number of teeth
- 2β = sprocket tooth angle $(360/N)$
- k = the number of engaged teeth (angle of wrap $\times$ N/360); round down to the nearest whole number to be safe

By this formula, if the chain is wrapped halfway around the sprocket, the back tension at sprocket tooth number six is only 0.96 N. This is 1 percent of the amount of a flat belt. Using chains and sprockets, the required back tension is much lower than a flat belt.

Now let's compare chains and sprockets with a toothed-belt back tension.

Although in toothed belts the allowable tension can differ with the number of pulley teeth and the revolutions per minute (rpm), the general recommendation is to use 1/3.5 of the allowable tension as the back tension (F). This is shown in Figure 2.8. Therefore, our 257 N force will require 257/3.5 = 73 N of back tension.

Both toothed belts and chains engage by means of teeth, but chain's back tension is only 1/75 that of toothed belts.

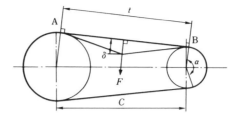

Back Tension on a Toothed Belt

2. Chain wear and jumping sprocket teeth

The key factor causing chain to jump sprocket teeth is chain wear elongation (see Basics Section 2.2.4). Because of wear elongation, the chain creeps up on the sprocket teeth until it starts jumping sprocket teeth and can no longer engage with the sprocket. Figure 2.9 shows sprocket tooth shape and positions of engagement. Figure 2.10 shows the engagement of a sprocket with an elongated chain.

In Figure 2.9 there are three sections on the sprocket tooth face:
- a: Bottom curve of tooth, where the roller falls into place;
- b: Working curve, where the roller and the sprocket are working together;
- c: Where the tooth can guide the roller but can't transmit tension. If the roller, which should transmit tension, only engages with C, it causes jumped sprocket teeth.

The chain's wear elongation limit varies according to the number of sprocket teeth and their shape, as shown in Figure 2.11. Upon calculation, we see that sprockets with large numbers of teeth are very limited in stretch percentage. Smaller sprockets are limited by other harmful effects, such as high vibration and decreasing strength; therefore, in the case of less than 60 teeth, the stretch limit ratio is limited to 1.5 percent (in transmission chain).

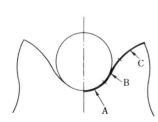

Sprocket Tooth Shape and Positions of Engagement

The Engagement Between a Sprocket and an Elongated Chain

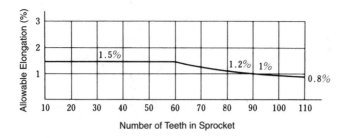

Figure 2.11 Elongation Versus the Number of Sprocket Teeth

In conveyor chains, in which the number of working teeth in sprockets is less than transmission chains, the stretch ratio is limited to 2 percent. Large pitch conveyor chains use a straight line in place of curve B in the sprocket tooth face.

2.2 CHAIN DRIVE IN ACTION

Let's study the case of an endless chain rotating on two sprockets (Figure 2.12).

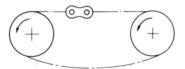

Figure 2.12   An Endless Chain Rotating Around Two Sprockets

2.2.1 Chordal Action

You will find that the position in which the chain and the sprockets engage fluctuates, and the chain vibrates along with this fluctuation. Even with the same chain, if you increase the number of teeth in the sprockets (change to larger diameter), vibration will be reduced. Decrease the number of teeth in the sprockets and vibration will increase.

This is because there is a pitch length in chains, and they can only bend at the pitch point. In Figure 2.13, the height of engagement (the radius from the center of the sprocket) differs when the chain engages in a tangent position and when it engages in a chord.

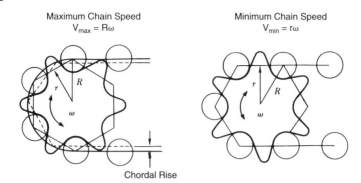

Maximum Chain Speed
$V_{max} = R\omega$

Minimum Chain Speed
$V_{min} = r\omega$

Chordal Rise

Figure 2.13 The Height of Engagement

Therefore, even when the sprockets rotate at the same speed, the chain speed is not steady according to a ratio of the sprocket radius (with chordal action). Chordal action is based on the number of teeth in the sprockets:

Ratio of speed change = $(V_{max} - V_{min}) / V_{max} = 1 - \cos (180°/N)$

Figure 2.14 shows the result. In addition to the number of teeth, if the shaft center distance is a common multiple of the chain pitch, chordal action is small. On the other hand, if shaft center distance is a multiple of chain pitch + 0.5 pitch, chordal action increases. Manufacturing and alignment errors can also impact chordal action.

In a flat-belt power transmission machine, if the thickness and bending elasticity of the belt are regular, there is no chordal action. But in toothed-belt systems, chordal action occurs by circle and chord, the same as chains. Generally this effect is less than 0.6 percent, but when combined with the deflection of the pulley center and errors of belt pitch or pulley pitch, it can amount to 2 to 3 percent.

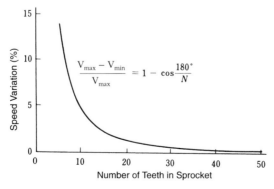

$$\frac{V_{max} - V_{min}}{V_{max}} = 1 - \cos\frac{180°}{N}$$

Figure 2.14 Speed Variation Versus the Number of Sprocket Teeth

2.2.2 Repeated Load Tension, Fatigue Failure

In Basics Section 2.2.1, we looked at the case of rotating chains without load. In this section, we'll examine rotating chains with load, a typical use of chains.

In Figure 2.15, the left sprocket is the driving side (power input) and the right sprocket is the driven side (power output). If we apply counterclockwise rotation power to the driving sprocket while adding resistance to the driven sprocket, then the chain is loaded in tension mainly at the D~A span, and tension is smaller in the other parts. Figure 2.16 shows this relation.

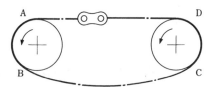

Figure 2.15   A Typical Chain Drive with the Driving Side on the Left

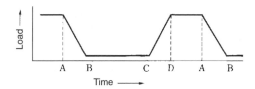

Figure 2.16   Chain Load with the Addition of Resistance

Chains in most applications are typically loaded by cyclical tension. Chain fatigue is tested under pulsating tension via a fixture. The fatigue limit will occur between 10^6 to 10^7 times. Figure 2.17 shows the concept of repeated load tension, where P_a represents the amplitude.

> NOTE: If the minimum force is zero, the chain is free to move during testing. Therefore, JIS provides $P_{min} = P_{max} \times 1/11$, as in Figure 2.17.

When a chain that is more than five links and of linear configuration receives repeated load, it can be shown as a solid line (as in Figure 2.17). JIS B 1801-1990 defines the breakage load in 5×10^6 times:

$$P_{max} = P_m + P_a = 2.2\ P_a$$

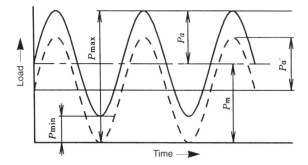

Figure 2.17   Repeated Load Tension

as the maximum allowable load. Figure 2.18 shows one result of fatigue examination in this way. In the figure, the vertical axis is P_{max} and the horizontal axis is the number of repetitions. When the repetitions are less than 10^4 times, the test results fluctuate greatly. Therefore, these figures are practically useless, and are not shown here.

In the previous paragraph, we need to be alert to what the JIS regulation is really saying: "JIS B 1801-1990 defines...P_{max} = 2.2 P_a as the maximum allowable load." This is set up with wrapping transmission as a model (as shown in Figure 2.15), and with the supposition that the smaller load side tension is 10 percent of the larger load side tension.

In actual practice, even if we use wrapping transmission, the smaller load side tension may be almost zero; and in the case of hanging or lifting, the chain's slack side also doesn't receive any load. In these cases, the conditions can be shown as a dotted line (Figure 2.17); chain load = 2 $P_{a'}$ and P_{min} = 0; therefore $2P_{a'} < P_{max}$.

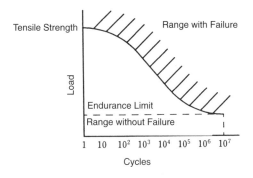

Figure 2.18   Fatigue Strength

18

If you follow the JIS definition of P_{max} as maximum allowable load and you choose a chain on the higher limits of the scale, the chain might not stand up to those strength requirements. In some situations a fatigue failure might occur even though it met the JIS requirement for maximum allowable load.

This is the reason that some manufacturers, such as Tsubaki, use $2P_a$ as the maximum allowable load; or some manufacturers calculate $2P_a$ under the situation of $P_{min} = 0$ and show this in their catalog. In the latter method, the $2P_{a'}$ value is larger than the value of the former method. The maximum allowable load value of the JIS method is 10 percent greater than the former method of $2P_a$.

In addition, some manufacturers, including Tsubaki, establish a fatigue limit for strength at 10^7 cycles. JIS sets a fatigue strength at 5×10^6 cycles.

Including the JIS scale, there are more than three ways of expressing the same information in manufacturers' catalogs. Therefore, you should not make a final determination about a chain's functions simply by depending on information found in different catalogs. Consider a manufacturer's reliability by checking whether they have their own fatigue-testing equipment. Ask if they show fatigue limit data in their catalogs. The quality guarantee system of ISO 9000 series is checked by third parties (instead of users) to gauge whether or not their system of quality guarantee is adequate. It would be safe to choose manufacturers who are ISO-9000-series certified.

2.2.3 Transmission Capability of Drive Chains

We have derived fatigue limits by testing. But just as you can't judge a person by examination alone, so we must also check whether the results of our tests can be put to practical use. Some questions remain:

1. The chain's fatigue limit (see Basics Section 2.2.2) is tested in a linear configuration (Figure 2.1). But in wrapping transmission, the chain is engaging with the sprocket. Is there any difference between these two?
2. A new roller chain is used. Is there any decrease in the strength of a used chain?
3. Do connecting links or offset links have the same strength?

To answer these questions, a number of experiments and investigations were done. The following are the findings.

2.2.3.1 Difference Between Linear Tension and Wrapping

When the chain engages the sprocket, the chain collides with the sprocket tooth surfaces. The transmission capability is limited by the roller or bushing breakage during collision.

As it wraps on the sprocket and rotates, the chain receives centrifugal force. The faster the speed of rotation, the larger the centrifugal force becomes. Additionally, the pin and the bushing are also subject to tension. There is a limit to their bearing function.

2.2.3.2 Effect of Normal Chain Wear on Fatigue Strength

When a chain is operating, the outer surface of the pin and inner surface of the bushing rub against one another, wearing little by little. (Proper lubrication reduces the amount of wear but does not eliminate it.)

The problem is the wear of the pin. As the surface of the pin is reduced, the rigidity of the pin decreases and eventually fatigue failure may result. The question is how much wear is acceptable and at what point should you be concerned.

Testing shows that when wear elongation is less than or equal to 1.5 percent for transmission chain, or less than or equal to 2 percent for conveyor chain, there is almost no risk of fatigue failure.

> NOTE: This replacment limit applies to situations in which every pin and bushing wears equally. If one part is subject to greater wear, the system should be examined and repaired. Chains should be replaced at the same time.

In practical terms, the most important consequence of deterioration is a decrease in the fatigue strength by environmental factors. This problem will be discussed in Basics Section 5.4.

2.2.3.3 Strength Differences Between Chain and the Connecting Links and Offset Links

The individual connecting links and offset links have lower fatigue strength than the chain itself. Therefore, you have to consider the strength-decrease ratio shown in Table 2.1. The strength-decrease ratio differs from manufacturer to manufacturer, so it is important to get specific information from each manufacturer.

Table 2.1 Strength Reduction of Connecting Links and Offset Links

Type	Reduction Ratio Against Maximum Allowable Load
Standard Connecting Link	0 ~ 20%
Tap Fit Connecting Link	No reduction
Offset Link	35%
Two-Pitch Offset Link	0 ~ 25%

If you use chain with loads that are almost the same as the maximum allowable load, you should avoid using offset links. Use tap fit connecting links, which are stronger than standard connecting links. In some cases, you can order chains in an endless configuration (see *NOTE* on next page).

NOTE: Endless configuration: Manufacturers create connecting components that are as strong as the chain's other parts by riveting or other factory processes. The chain is assembled and delivered as an endless configuration.

The transmission-ability graph, which is sometimes called a "tent curve" because of its shape, includes the result of the three points covered above. This graph is an important tool when making chain decisions. Figure 2.19 illustrates the concept of a tent curve.

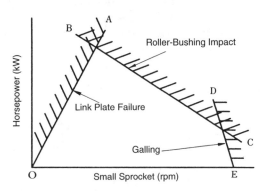

A Transmission-Ability Graph (Tent Curve)

In Figure 2.19, Line O-A is decided according to the chain's allowable tension, which includes the fatigue strength of the connecting or offset links, as well as the centrifugal force in high-speed rotation. Line B-C is decided by breakage limit of the bushing and roller. In this kind of breakage of the bushing and roller, there is no fatigue limit as there is with the link plates. Therefore, it is shown within 15,000 hours of strength-in-limited-duration. Line D-E is decided by the bearing function of the pin and the bushing.

The range defined within these three lines (O-A, B-C, and D-E) is the usable range. When the chain is used at low speeds, it is limited by line O-A, the fatigue limit. The conditions of the tent curve shown are:
   a. Two-shaft wrapping transmission with 100 links of chain.
   b. Duration of 15,000 hours work.
   c. Under the Additional Operating Conditions (1 through 5 shown below).

Additional Operating Conditions
   1. The chain operates in an indoor environment of -10°C to 60°C, and there is no abrasive dust.
   2. There are no effects from corrosive gas or high humidity.
   3. The two driving shafts are parallel with each other and adjusted properly.
   4. Lubrication is applied as recommended in the catalog.
   5. The transmission is subject to only small fluctuations in load.

2.2.4 Wear of Working Parts

In Basics Section 2.2.3.2, we discussed the effects of pin wear. When a chain is operating, the outer surface of the pin and inner surface of the bushing rub against one another, wearing little by little.

When a chain is operating, obviously other parts are also moving and wearing. For example, the outer surface of the bushing and inner surface of the roller move against one another. In the case of transmission chain, the roller and bushing wear is less than that of the pin and the inner surface of the bushing because the chance of rubbing is generally smaller. Also, it is easier to apply lubrication between the bushing and roller.

The progress of pin-bushing wear is shown in Figure 2.20, in which the horizontal axis is the working hours and the vertical axis is the wear elongation (percent of chain length).

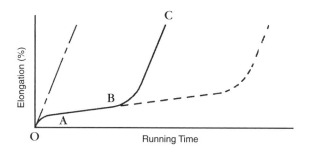

| Figure 2.20 | Pin-Bushing Wear During Operation |

In Figure 2.20, O-A is called "initial wear." At first the wear progresses rapidly, but its ratio is less than 0.1 percent and usually it will cease within 20 hours of continuous operation. A-B is "normal wear." Its progress is slow. B-C is "extreme wear." The limit of "allowable wear" (the end of its useful life) will be reached during this stage (1.5 to 2.0 percent).

The solid line reflects a case of using chain with working parts that were lubricated in the factory, but were not lubricated again. If you lubricate regularly, the pin and the bushing continue to exhibit normal wear (reflected by the dotted line), and eventually run out their useful life.

If you remove all the lubricants with solvents, the wear progresses along a nearly straight line, and the life of the chain is shortened. This is shown by the dashed line.

The factors that affect chain wear are very complicated. There are many considerations, such as lubrication, assembly accuracy, condition of produced parts, and the method of producing parts; therefore, wear value can't be greatly improved by merely changing one factor.

In transmission chain, JIS B 1801-1990 regulates the surface hardness of the pin, the bushing, and the roller (as shown in Table 2.2) to meet the multiple requirements for wear resistance and shock resistance.

Table 2.2. Surface Hardness of Pin, Bushing, and Roller

Component	HV	HRC
Pin	450 or greater	45 or greater
Bushing	450 or greater	45 or greater
Roller	390 or greater	40 or greater

2.2.5 Noise and Vibration

When the chain engages the sprockets, it will definitely make noise (Figure 2.21). This is caused by several factors:

1. The chain roller strikes the sprocket tooth bottom.
2. There is space between the roller and the bushing; the roller makes noise by its elastic vibration (in the case of thin rollers, like S-roller).
3. Sprockets vibrate.
4. The fluid held between each part (usually air or lubrication oil) makes shock sounds.

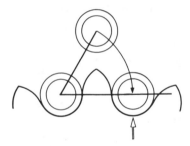

Figure 2.21   Noise Occurs when the Chain Engages the Sprocket

Take for example, an RS80 transmission roller chain and a sprocket with 16 teeth operating at a speed of 123 rpm. (The chain speed is 50 m/min.) In this case, the noise at a point 30 cm from the sprocket will be: with no lubrication, 65 dB (A); with lubrication, 57 dB (A).

According to the data given above, the noise made by the chain engaging the sprocket can be predicted. Please contact the manufacturer.

There are some steps you can take to lessen the noise level.

    a. Decrease striking energy:
- Use a sprocket with many teeth. This reduces the impact velocity while maintaining the same chain speed.
- Operate the chain at slower speeds.
- Use smaller chain to decrease the chain's weight.

b. Buffer the effects of the impacting parts:
   - Lubricate at the bottom of the sprocket tooth and the gap between the bushing and the roller.
   - Use specially engineered plastic rollers. (This will also decrease transmission capability. There is virtually no decrease in sound if you change to an engineered plastic sprocket.)

If we compare noise from chains and sprockets with other transmission machine parts like belt and pulley or toothed belt and pulley, we find:
   a. Belt noise is less than the other two. Compared to a flat belt, a toothed belt makes a high frequency noise during high speed.
   b. Usually, chain transmission is smoother than gear transmission. The chain also differs in that there is no increase in noise level as it wears and elongates during use.

2.3 CHARACTERISTIC PHENOMENA IN CONVEYOR CHAIN

Until now, we have primarily been explaining matters that apply specifically to power transmission chains. However, there are some different problems that occur when using conveyor chain.

2.3.1 Coefficient of Friction

The tension of transmission chain is calculated by dividing the transmitted power (indicated as kW or horsepower) by the chain speed and multiplying by an adequate coefficient. But in a fixed-speed, horizontal conveyor, tension is decided by those factors shown below:
1. The coefficient of friction between the chain and the rail when conveyed objects are placed on the chain.
2. The coefficient of friction between conveyed objects and the rail when conveyed objects are held on the rail and pushed by the chain.

   NOTE: There are two types of tension: the first occurs when conveyed objects are moving at a fixed speed, and the second is inertial effects that occur when starting and stopping the machine. We will only talk about the former in this section, and the latter in Basics Section 2.3.2.

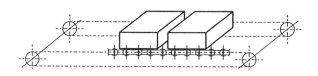

Figure 2.22   Tension on a Horizontal Conveyor

The tension (T) in a horizontal conveyor, like that in Figure 2.22, is basically calculated by this formula:

$$T = M_1 \times g \times f_1 \times 1.1 + M_1 \times g \times f_2 + M_2 \times g \times f_3$$

Where:

T = total chain tension
M_1 = weight of the chain, etc.
M_2 = weight of conveyed objects
f_1 = coefficient of friction when chain, etc., are returning
f_2 = coefficient of friction when chain, etc., are conveying
f_3 = coefficient of friction when conveyed objects are moving
g = gravitational constant
1.1 = sprocket losses due to directional changes of the chain

NOTE: "chain, etc.," in the above formula includes chain and the parts moving with the chain, such as attachments and slats.

In this formula, a coefficient of friction is multiplied by every term in the equation. Therefore, if the coefficient of friction is high, the tension increases and larger chain is required. Also, the necessary motor power, which is calculated as tension × speed × coefficient, increases. A more powerful motor is needed when the coefficient of friction is high.

Reduce the coefficient of friction and you can reduce the tension, too. This allows you to choose a more economical chain and motor, and decrease the initial and running costs for conveyor equipment.

The chain's coefficient of friction differs by type of chain, by material, and by type of roller; it is shown in the manufacturer's catalog. To illustrate this concept, two examples are included. The coefficient of friction for different types of top chain and guide rails is shown in Table 2.3. The coefficient of friction when large R-roller chain rotates on rails (rail material: steel) is shown in Table 2.4.

Table 2.3 Friction Coefficients for Top Plate and Guide Rails

		Friction Coefficient	
Top Plate Material	**Guide Rail Material**	**Unlubricated**	**Lubricated**
Stainless Steel or Steel	Stainless Steel or Steel	0.35	0.20
Stainless Steel or Steel	UHMW	0.25	0.15
Engineered Plastic	Stainless Steel or Steel	0.25	0.15
Engineered Plastic	UHMW	0.25	0.12
Engineered Plastic (Low Friction)	Stainless Steel or Steel	0.17	0.12
Engineered Plastic (Low Friction)	UHMW	0.18	0.12

Table 2.4 Friction Coefficients for Different Types of Rollers

		Friction Coefficient	
Chain Type	**Roller Type**	**Unlubricated**	**Lubricated**
RF Double Pitch Chain	Steel	0.12	0.08
	Engineered Plastic	0.08	—
Large Pitch Conveyor Chain	Steel	0.13 ~ 0.15	0.08
	Engineered Plastic	0.08	—
	Bearing Roller	0.03	—

Technology can help you reduce the coefficient of friction. Some of the newest chains (for example, low-friction top chain, engineered plastic roller chain, and bearing roller chain) can achieve low coefficients of friction without lubrication. Other chains would have to be lubricated to achieve these coefficients. In some instances, these new chains achieve dramatically lower coefficients of friction. That means you can save maintenance time, money, and energy at your facility.

2.3.2 Dynamic Tension of Starting and Stopping

Conveyor chain accelerates when it changes from stop mode to operational speeds, and decelerates when it changes from operational speeds to stop modes. Therefore, a dynamic tension resulting from inertia affects the conveyor chain, and it is added to "the tension produced when conveyed objects are moving at fixed speed," which is discussed in Basics Section 2.3.1. You must consider dynamic tension caused by inertia, especially in the following cases:

1. Starting and stopping chains frequently, such as intermittent use with indexing equipment.
2. Starting and stopping in very short time spans.
3. When chains in motion suddenly receive stationary objects to convey.

The dynamic tension by inertia is calculated with this formula:

$$T_1 = M \times \alpha = M \times \frac{dv}{dt}$$

Where:

M = total weight of conveying apparatus, including chain, attachments, product, etc., (kg)
α = maximum acceleration (m/s²)
dv = change in speed (m/s)
dt = time in which speed change occurs (s)

For example:

M = 5,000 kg, the total weight of chain, attachment, product, etc.
f = 0.12, the dynamic coefficient of friction
T = 5,000 × 9.8 × 0.12 = 5,880 N

This assumes the conveyor is operating at constant speed. But when the chain starts, if the speed is increased to 20 m/min. in 0.2 seconds, then:

dv = 20/60 = 0.33 m/s

dt = 0.2 s

$$T_1 = 5,000 \times \frac{0.33}{0.2} = 8,250 \text{ N}$$

Maximum tension = $T + T_1$ = 14,130 N

If the chain is accelerated frequently in this manner, then select chains using $T + T_1$.

2.3.3 Wear Between Rollers and Bushings

During the operation of conveyor chains, rollers receive some additional forces, which are shown in Figure 2.23 and listed below:

1. The weight of conveyed objects when they are put directly on the chain.
2. The reaction forces when pushing conveyed objects with a dog.
3. Directional variation tension when the rail is set in a curved path.

These forces cause wear between rollers and bushings.

Some manufacturers publish an "allowable roller load"—a value at which the wear rate of the roller is comparatively slow. For steel rollers, it is the value with lubrication. For engineered plastic rollers and bearing rollers, the values shown are without lubrication. Sometimes, engineered plastic rollers may be affected by speed. Please check the catalogs.

If foreign objects, including conveyed objects, get into the working parts of the chain, the catalog values are no longer applicable, even if you are using lubrication.

There are many conveyed objects that work as lubricants; therefore, it is hard to generalize about the allowable roller loads when there are any foreign objects that might get into the working parts. Furthermore, the loads on the rollers (as shown in points 1 through 3 above), are also applicable to the side rollers and to the resulting wear of pins and side rollers. Make sure you consider these factors when setting up a conveyor system.

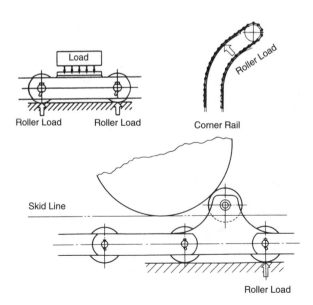

 Forces on Conveyor Rollers

2.3.4 Strength of Attachments

Bending and twisting forces can affect the attachments. For the A attachment, which is a common type, the allowable load calculation indicated in catalogs is based on the bending strength.

When a tall fixture is added onto the attachment, you must study the strength of the entire configuration. When the attachment is subject to forces other than those explained, you also must calculate the twisting forces. If the attachment receives bending forces at the same time, make sure to combine the bending forces with the twisting forces.

When calculating the strength of attachments such as A-type, K-type, SA-type, and SK-type, which are extensions of a standard steel chain's plate, use the values shown below as their ultimate tensile strength, and choose a proper safety factor.

Nonheat-treated plate: 490 MPa (50 kgf/mm²)
Heat-treated plate: 1,078 MPa (110 kgf/mm²)

2.3.5 Stick Slip

When using an extra-long conveyor system (more than 15 m) and slow chain speed (less than 10 m/min.), you may notice longitudinal vibration in the line, which is called stick slip, or jerking.

The basis for this phenomenon can be seen in Figure 2.24. Here the coefficient of friction is plotted against the speed of the chain. When operating a long conveyor at slow speeds, the coefficient of friction for sliding surfaces (in top chains, between top plates and rails; in R-rollers, between the outer surface of the bushing and inner surface of the roller) decreases as speed increases. This causes the chain to jerk or stick slip.

Usually, you can't solve this problem by adding lubrication or by increasing the number of sprocket teeth. There are, however, things you can do to prevent or reduce stick slip:

1. Increase chain speed.

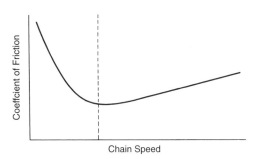

Figure 2.24   How Chain Speed Impacts the Friction Coefficient

2. Eliminate or decrease the decline in the coefficient of friction by using a bearing roller (please consult with manufacturer if the speed is less than 2 m/min.), or use a special kind of lubrication oil (Tsubaki special oil, or others).

3. Increase chain rigidity (AE). A is the chain's section area, and E is Young's modulus. To increase AE, use a larger chain. If there are several chains with the same allowable tension, choose the one with the thicker plate.

4. Separate the conveyor into sections and reduce the length of each machine.

If stick slip continues to be a problem, consult the equipment manufacturer.

2.3.6 Relative Differences in Chain's Total Length

If you want to achieve a precise positioning of more than two chain lines to be used in parallel, you can order "matched and tagged" chain. Generally, if the conveyor chains are made in the same lots, the relative differences in length will vary only slightly. Table 2.5 shows the amount of variation for several types of chain chosen at random from the same production run.

If your specific application requires less variation than those listed in Table 2.5, consider matched and tagged chains as an effective solution.

Table 2.5 Conveyor Chains Chosen at Random from Same Production Lot

Center Distance	Matched Tolerance
Less than 7 m	Less than 3 mm
7 ~ 15 m	Less than 4 mm
15 ~ 22 m	Less than 5 mm

2.3.7 Take-Up

Conveyor chains need proper tension, which is why take-up is added to a system. You have to position take-up where the chain's tension will be minimal. If you can remove two links from the chain, the adjusting length of take-up is:

L = chain pitch + spare length

If you can't remove links from the chain, use this formula:

L = length of machine $\times$ 0.02 + spare length

In this formula, 0.02 represents the allowable wear value (2 percent). There are two portions of the spare length: one is the maximum and minimum range of variation in length for new chains; the other portion is the length to loosen the chain's connecting link when the chain's total length has been set as tight as possible. For example: the machine length is 10 m, the length for maximum and minimum range of variation is 0.25 percent, assuming the length needed to connect chain is 25 mm, then:

$L = 10{,}000 \times (0.02 + 0.0025) + 25 = 225 + 25 = 250$ (mm)

If the chain expands and contracts with temperature, the system needs some means to absorb it. When you use a chain in a high-temperature environment or to convey high-temperature objects, the chain becomes hotter and the length increases at about the same ratio as its coefficient of linear expansion. When the temperature is between 0° and 300°C, and 1 m of chain is heated by a value of 100°C, the chain elongates by about 1 mm. If you want to allow for this elongation with take-up, you must be careful about the following points or the chain may fail:

- In the case of chain temperature increase, adjust take-up after the temperature increase.
- In the case of chain temperature decrease, adjust take-up before the decrease.

In the case of chain temperature change, the take-up should be designed to absorb the elongation or the contraction of the chain.

If you don't drive the chain in reverse, it is more convenient to design a catenary section and collect the elongation in that part. In that case, it is also beneficial to design a take-up. Figure 2.25 shows an example of a design with catenary and take-up.

It is very annoying to continuously adjust take-up. Sometimes it is possible to use self-adjusting take-ups by hanging a weight or using a hydraulic power cylinder instead of adjusting the take-up. However, the chain receives additional tension by doing this (sometimes the motor capacity is also influenced), so don't forget to check the chain strength as well as the motor capacity.

Another point about take-up is that if you drive the chain in reverse while carrying objects, the take-up receives the load as if it were a driving part. In this situation, you must select and design take-up with consideration for its strength.

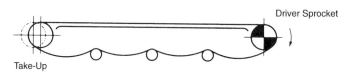

Driver Sprocket

Take-Up

Roller Catenary Support

Figure 2.25 Catenary Take-Up

3. PUBLIC STANDARDS OF CHAINS

Because chain is widely used throughout the world, there are both international and domestic standards to guarantee their interchangeability and functions. Table 3.1 shows the primary standards.

Table 3.1. Standards for Major Types of Chains[1]

Chain Category	ANSI Standard	ISO Standard	JIS Standard
Power Transmission Roller Chain	ANSI B 29.1M	ISO 606	JIS B 1801
Power Transmission Bushed Chain	ANSI B 29.1M	ISO 1395	JIS B 1801
Power Transmission Sprocket	ANSI B 29.1M	ISO 606	JIS B 1802
Heavy-Duty Chain	ANSI B 29.10M	ISO 3512	
Bicycle Chain		ISO 9633	JIS D 9417
Motorcycle Chain		ISO 10190	JCAS 1[2]
Leaf Chain	ANSI B 29.8M	ISO 4347	JIS B 1804
Double Pitch Conveyor Chain & Sprocket	ANSI B 29.4	ISO 1275	JIS B 1803
Power Transmission Roller Chain with Attachment	ANSI B 29.5		JIS B 1801
Conveyor Chain	ANSI B 29.15	ISO 1977/1~3	JCAS 2[2]

[1] The contents of each standard for a category may vary from group to group.
[2] JCAS indicates the Japanese Chain Association Standard.

4. HOW TO SELECT CHAINS

In this chapter, we outline the selection process. To choose the right chain, follow the step-by-step procedure for the type of line you're running. The first thing you must determine is the type of application: power transmission or conveyor. The selection process differs for the two applications; see Basics Sections 4.1 and 4.2.

In addition to the procedures described in this book, chain manufacturers usually provide comprehensive selection charts in their catalogs; refer to the manufacturer's catalog for detailed information.

4.1 TRANSMISSION CHAIN SELECTION

There are four main uses for transmission chains: power transmission, hanging transmission, shuttle traction, and pin-gear driving.

1. Power transmission. The most frequent application, power transmission involves an endless chain wrapped on two sprockets. There are two ways to select chains for this use.

For general applications, you can select by power transmission capability (tent curve). This is shown in Figure 4.1.

For slow-speed operation, you can make an economical selection using the maximum allowable tension. Use this method when chain speed is less than 50 m/min. and starting frequency is less than five times/day (Figure 4.2).

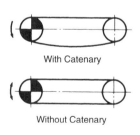

With Catenary

Without Catenary

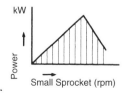

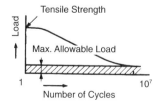

Figure 4.1   Power Transmission Capability

Figure 4.2   Maximum Allowable Load at Slow Speeds (less than 50 m/min.)

2. Hanging transmission. This design is increasing in popularity. It is used, for example, in parking garage elevators. Sprockets rotate, and conveyed objects can be lifted or suspended at the end of chains. (Figure 4.3).
3. Shuttle traction. (Figure 4.4).
4. Pin-gear drive. In this design, the chains are laid straight or in a large diameter circle and are driven with special tooth form sprockets. This design is more economical than using gears (Figure 4.5).

In this book, we will focus on items 1 and 2. Consult your manufacturer's catalog for information on items 3 and 4.

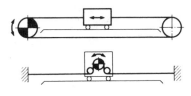

Figure 4.3 Hanging Transmission Where Conveyed Objects Are Lifted or Suspended at the End of Chains

Figure 4.4 Shuttle Traction

Figure 4.5 Pin-Gear Drive Transmission

4.1.1 Chain Selection Factors

You must consider the following conditions:
1. Type of application.
2. Shock load.
3. Source of power: motor type; rated power (kW); moment of inertia, I (kg • m^2); rated torque at driving speed; starting torque; and stopping torque.
4. Drive sprocket rpm and shaft diameter.
5. Driven sprocket rpm and shaft diameter.

6. Center distance between sprockets.
7. Noise constraints.
8. Lubrication (possible or not).

4.1.2 Coefficients Used in Selection

1. Multiple strand factor
   In multiple strand power transmission chains, the loading is unequal across the width of the chain, therefore, the transmission capability is not a direct multiple of the number of chains. You must use a "multiple strand factor," which is shown in Table 4.1, to determine the correct value.
2. Service factor, Ks
   The chain transmission capability is reduced if there are frequent or severe load fluctuations. You must apply the appropriate factor based on the type of machine or motors (Table 4.2).

Table 4.1 Multiple Strand Factor

Number of Roller Chain Strands	Multiple Strand Factor
2	1.7
3	2.5
4	3.3
5	3.9
6	4.6

Table 4.2 Service Factor

		Source of Power		
			Internal Combustion Engine	
Type of Impact	Machines	Electric Motor or Turbine	With Hydraulic Drive	Without Hydraulic Drive
Smooth	Belt conveyors with small load fluctuation, chain conveyors, centrifugal blowers, ordinary textile machines, ordinary machines with small load fluctuation.	1.0	1.0	1.2
Some impact	Centrifugal compressors, marine engines, conveyors with some load fluctuation, automatic furnaces, dryers, pulverizers, general machine tools, compressors, general work machines, general paper mills.	1.3	1.2	1.4
High impact	Press, construction or mining machines, vibration machines, oil-well rigs, rubber mixers, rolls, general machines with reverse or high-impact loads.	1.5	1.4	1.7

3. Chain speed coefficient, Kv; sprocket tooth coefficient, Kc
   Adjust the transmission capability according to the chain speed and
   number of teeth in the small sprocket (Figure 4.6). The sprocket
   coefficient is labeled Kc.
4. Impact coefficient, K
   This coefficient (Figure 4.7) is based on the inertia ratio of the driving
   machine and driven machine (ratio of I, ratio of GD^2) and the amount of
   play in transmission equipment. When the inertia ratio is less than 0.2 or
   greater than 10, use the value of 0.2 or 10, respectively.

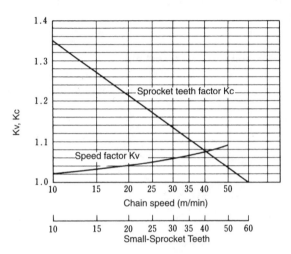

Figure 4.6   Speed Factor (Kv) and Sprocket Factor (Kc)

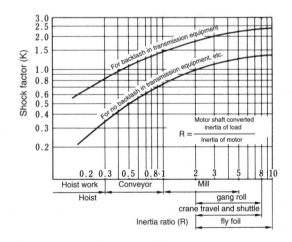

Figure 4.7   Shock Factor (K)

Table 4.3 Unbalanced Load Factor (Ku)

Lifting Strands	Factor
2	0.6
4	0.36

5. Unbalanced load coefficient; Ku
   When you use two or four chains in a hanging application or shuttle traction setup, the tension of each chain is not equal. This must be accounted for by using the coefficient found in Table 4.3. The example assumes an unbalanced load ratio between two chains of 60/40 (percent) [i.e., 60 + 40 = 100 percent].

4.1.3 Drive Chain Selection (General Selection)
A suitable chain selection may be made according to the flow chart Figure 4.8. EXAMPLE: Select a transmission chain for the conditions shown in Figure 4.9.

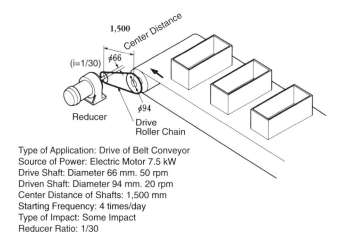

Type of Application: Drive of Belt Conveyor
Source of Power: Electric Motor 7.5 kW
Drive Shaft: Diameter 66 mm. 50 rpm
Driven Shaft: Diameter 94 mm. 20 rpm
Center Distance of Shafts: 1,500 mm
Starting Frequency: 4 times/day
Type of Impact: Some Impact
Reducer Ratio: 1/30

Figure 4.9 Operating Conditions for Example 4.1.3

Step 1. Confirm the operating conditions.
Step 2. Determine the service factor K_s as shown in Table 4.2. In this example, the service factor is K_s = 1.3.
Step 3. Calculate the corrected design power kW = 1.3 × 7.5 = 9.75 kW.
Step 4. Consult the selection table (Figure 4.10). For n = 50 rpm and corrected power = 9.75 kW, you should initially select RS140 chain and a 15-tooth drive sprocket. These are not the final selections. See manufacturer's catalog for additional information.

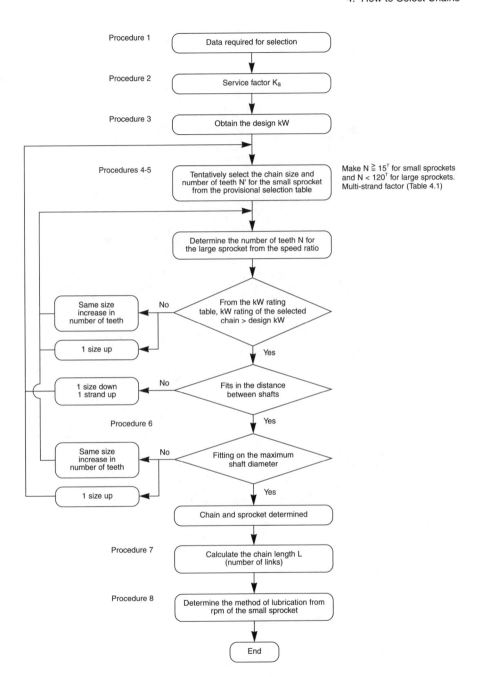

Procedure 1 — Data required for selection

Procedure 2 — Service factor K_s

Procedure 3 — Obtain the design kW

Procedures 4-5 — Tentatively select the chain size and number of teeth N' for the small sprocket from the provisional selection table

Make N ≧ 15^T for small sprockets and N < 120^T for large sprockets. Multi-strand factor (Table 4.1)

Determine the number of teeth N for the large sprocket from the speed ratio

From the kW rating table, kW rating of the selected chain > design kW — No → Same size increase in number of teeth; 1 size up

Fits in the distance between shafts — No → 1 size down 1 strand up

Procedure 6

Fitting on the maximum shaft diameter — No → Same size increase in number of teeth; 1 size up

Chain and sprocket determined

Procedure 7 — Calculate the chain length L (number of links)

Procedure 8 — Determine the method of lubrication from rpm of the small sprocket

End

Figure 4.8 Chain Selection Procedure (General Selection)

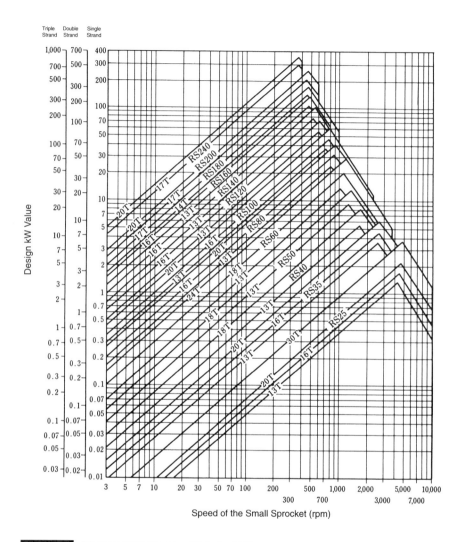

Figure 4.10 RS Roller Chain Provisional Selection Table

Step 4a. Calculate the size of the driven sprocket. Number of teeth in driven sprocket = 15 × (50/20) = 37.5. Therefore, select a 38-tooth driven sprocket.

Step 4b. Confirm that the chain meets the power requirements. According to the power transmission tables in the catalog, an RS140 chain with a 15-tooth sprocket is capable of transmitting 11.3 kW. Because 11.3 kW is greater than the design power of 9.75 kW, it is acceptable.

Step 5. Confirm that you can set a 15-tooth sprocket and a 38-tooth sprocket within the 1,500-mm center distance and still maintain clearance. The maximum hub bores of each sprocket are 89 and 110, respectively. Therefore, these may be used.

Step 6. Calculate L, the number of chain pitches.

$$C = \frac{\text{center distance}}{\text{chain pitch}}$$

$$C = \frac{1,500}{44.45} = 33.746 \text{ (sprocket center distance, in pitches)}$$

$$L = \frac{(N + N')}{2} + 2C + \frac{\left(\frac{N - N'}{6.28}\right)^2}{C} = \frac{(38 + 15)}{2} + 2 \times 33.746 + \frac{\left(\frac{38 - 15}{6.28}\right)^2}{33.746}$$

$$= 94.39 \text{ links}$$

Because you can't have fractions of links, choose the next highest even number. In this example, you would use 96 pitches. The center distance of the sprockets will then be 1,536 mm.

Step 7. Check the catalog and decide the appropriate type of lubrication (manual or drip).

4.1.4 Power Transmission Chain Selection for Slow Speeds

This selection procedure is based on the maximum allowable tension, which is used when the chain speed is less than 50 m/min., and the starting frequency is less than 5 times/day. The selection is done following the flow chart in Figure 4.11.

EXAMPLE: Recalculate the previous example from Basics Section 4.1.3 based upon the selection for slow speed.

Step 1. Tentatively select RS120 chain, which is one size smaller than RS140, and a 15-tooth sprocket. Then calculate the chain speed.
$V = PNn / 1,000 = (38.1 \times 15 \times 50)/ 1,000 = 28.6$ m/min. < 50
According to this speed and starting frequency, case selection for slow speed may be used.

Step 2. From the rated power of the motor, calculate the tension Fm on the chain.
$Fm = 60 \times kW / V = 60 \times 7.5 / 28.6 = 15.7$ kN

Step 3. Service factor $Ks = 1.3$, Chain speed coefficient $Kv = 1.06$ (from the chain speed 28.6 m/min.).

Step 4. Sprocket tooth coefficient $Kc = 1.27$ (from 15-tooth sprocket).

Step 5. Calculate the design chain tension F'm.
$F'm = Fm \times 1.3 \times 1.06 \times 1.27 = 27.5$ kN

Step 6. Decide on the chain size.

Basics

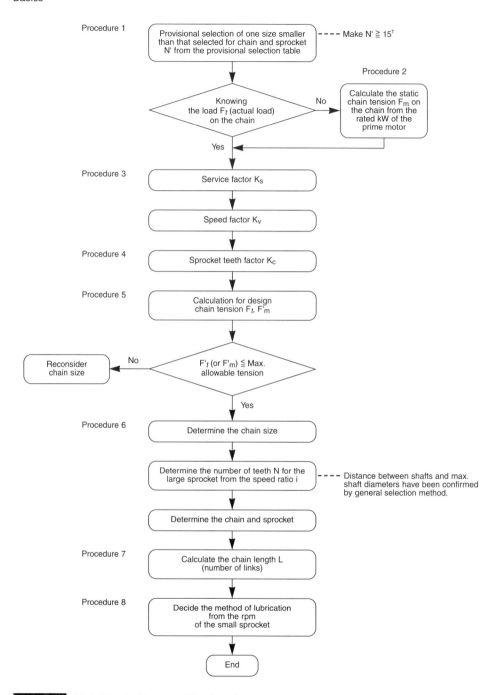

Procedure 1 — Provisional selection of one size smaller than that selected for chain and sprocket N' from the provisional selection table ---- Make N' $\geqq 15^T$

Knowing the load F_t (actual load) on the chain — No → Procedure 2 — Calculate the static chain tension F_m on the chain from the rated kW of the prime motor

Yes

Procedure 3 — Service factor K_s

Speed factor K_v

Procedure 4 — Sprocket teeth factor K_c

Procedure 5 — Calculation for design chain tension F_t, F'_m

F'_t (or F'_m) $\leqq$ Max. allowable tension — No → Reconsider chain size

Yes

Procedure 6 — Determine the chain size

Determine the number of teeth N for the large sprocket from the speed ratio i ---- Distance between shafts and max. shaft diameters have been confirmed by general selection method.

Determine the chain and sprocket

Procedure 7 — Calculate the chain length L (number of links)

Procedure 8 — Decide the method of lubrication from the rpm of the small sprocket

End

Figure 4.11 Chain Selection Procedure (Slow Speed)

According to the catalog, the maximum allowable load of RS120 is 30.4 kN. Because this value is higher than the chain design tension determined in Step 5, RS120 may be used in this application.

Select the number of teeth in the large sprocket according to the speed ratio, using the same procedure as in the general selection.

Confirm the chain and the sprocket: driving sprocket is RS120-15T (maximum hub bore is 80 mm, and the shaft diameter is 66 mm; therefore, this may be used), and driven sprocket is RS120-38T (maximum hub bore is not shown in catalogs). Therefore, consult with the manufacturer and determine that the 38-tooth sprocket will accommodate a 94-mm shaft.

Step 7. Calculate the chain length (number of links).

$$C = \frac{1,500}{38.10} = 39.37 \text{ mm}$$

$$L = \frac{(N + N')}{2} + 2C + \frac{\left(\frac{N - N'}{6.28}\right)^2}{C} = \frac{(38 + 15)}{2} + 2 \times 39.37 + \frac{\left(\frac{38 - 15}{6.28}\right)^2}{39.37}$$
$$= 105.58 \text{ links}$$

Therefore, use 106 links. Center distance = 1,508 mm.

Step 8. Check the manufacturer's catalog to determine the necessary type of lubrication (manual or drip).

As you see, this selection allows you to choose a smaller and more economical chain than the general selection. But, at the same time, consider these facts:

- Do not use offset links or normal connecting links for slow speeds. Use tap fit connecting links, which have a tight interference fit. If you want to use offset links or normal connecting links, check the strength derating shown in Basics Section 2.2.3 and recalculate.
- Cast-iron sprockets are not strong enough for slow speeds. Therefore, use SS400, S35C, S45C, etc.
- Use a hardened-tooth sprocket for the high-speed sprocket.
- The bearing pressure on the chain will be very high, so lubricate the chain well.

4.1.5 Hanging Transmission Chain Selection

Calculate the chain tension on both the load side and the driving side, and select a chain with a suitable maximum allowable tension to satisfy the requirements. The points of notice are shown below.

- If there are any laws or guidelines for chain selection, check and calculate accordingly. Make sure to follow the manufacturer's selections, and select the safer one of the two selections.

- The chain speed should be less than 50 m/min. If it is more than 50 m/min., consult the manufacturer.
- Use tap fit connecting links that have a tight interference fit. When you want to use normal connecting links or offset links, you must apply the appropriate derating value (Basics Section 2.2.3) to the chain strength.
- Lubricate the chain joints as much as possible after you reduce the loads. Lubrication is also required at terminal connections, etc.
- Make sure to follow proper safety procedures, including:
  a. Be sure that no one is under the suspended objects.
  b. Install a reliable safety guard to avoid damage in the event of chain failure.
  c. Examine chains regularly, and replace when necessary.

Figure 4.12 shows some common examples of hanging use. Selection is done according to the flow chart in Figure 4.13.

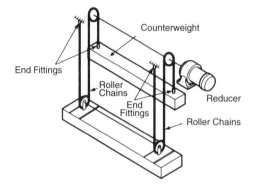

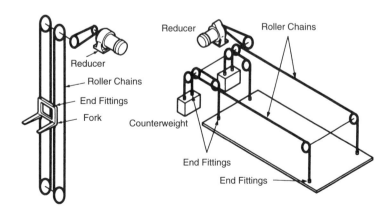

Figure 4.12 Typical Configurations for Hanging Chain

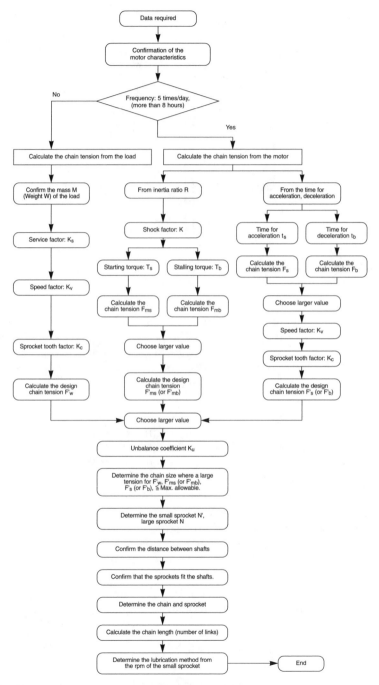

Figure 4.13 Chain Selection Procedure (Hanging Chain)

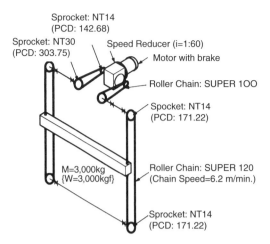

Figure 4.14 Example of a Hanging Chain Machine

EXAMPLE: You are planning to use a hanging transmission machine like the one shown in Figure 4.14. Determine if you can use SUPER120 for hanging and SUPER100 for the drive chain. The power source is a 3.7-kW motor (with brake). The motor shaft rotational speed is 1,500 rpm.

Step 1. Check the motor characteristics.
   Rated torque: T_n = 0.038 kN • m
   Starting torque: T_s = 0.083 kN • m
   Braking torque: T_b = 0.096 kN • m
   Motor moment of inertia: I_m = 0.015 kN • m

Step 2. Calculate the chain tension based on load.
   The chain tension $Fw = M$ = 3,000 × 9.80665 × 10^{-3} = 29.4 kN
   Service factor Ks = 1.3 (with some shock)
   The chain speed coefficient Kv = 1.02 (from the chain speed 6.2 m/min.)
   Coefficient for number of sprocket teeth Kc = 1.28 (14-tooth sprocket)
   Coefficient of unbalanced load Ku = 0.6 (two sets of chains)
   Determine the chain design tension
      $F'w = Fw \times Ks \times Kv \times Kc \times Ku$
         = 29.4 × 1.3 × 1.02 × 1.28 × 0.6 = 29.9 kN

Step 3. Calculate the chain tension based on the motor loading. Calculate moment of inertia of motor shaft.

$$I = M \times \left(\frac{V}{2\pi n_1}\right)^2 = 3{,}000 \times \left(\frac{6.2}{2 \times \pi \times 1{,}500}\right)^2 = 0.0013 \text{ kg} \bullet \text{m}^2$$

Moment of inertia of motor I_m = 0.015 kg • m^2
Inertia ratio $R = I / I_m$ = 0.087

When there is no play in the system, the coefficient of shock $K = 0.23$ (Figure 4.7). The chain tension from the starting torque:

$$Fms = Ts \times i \times \frac{30}{14} \times 1,000 / (d/2)$$

$$= 0.083 \times 60 \times \frac{30}{14} \times 1,000 / (171.22/2) = 124.7 \text{ kN}$$

The chain tension calculated from the braking torque:

$$Fmb = Tb \times i \times \frac{30}{14} \times 1,000 \times 1.2 / (d/2)$$

$$= 0.096 \times 60 \times \frac{30}{14} \times 1,000 \times 1.2 / (171.22/2) = 173.0 \text{ kN}$$

Use the larger value (in this case it is Fmb) to calculate chain tension.

$$F'mb = Fmb \times Kv \times Kc \times Ku \times K$$
$$= 173.0 \times 1.02 \times 1.28 \times 0.6 \times 0.23 = 31.2 \text{ kN}$$

Step 4. Calculate the chain tension from motor acceleration and deceleration.

$$\text{Working torque } Tm = \frac{(Ts + Tb)}{2} = \frac{(0.083 + 0.096)}{2} = 0.0895 \text{ kN} \bullet \text{m}$$

$$\text{Load torque } T_L = \frac{M \times d}{(2 \times 1,000 \times i)} \times \frac{g}{1,000}$$

$$= \frac{(3,000 \times 171.22)}{2 \times 1,000 \times 60 \times \frac{30}{14}} \times \frac{g}{1,000} = 0.02 \text{ kN} \bullet \text{m}$$

$$\text{Motor acceleration time } t_s = \frac{(Im + Il) \times n_1}{375 \times (Tm - Tl)} \times \frac{g}{1,000} \times 4$$

$$= \frac{(0.015 + 0.00130) \times 1,500}{375 \times (0.0895 - 0.02)} \times \frac{g}{1,000} \times 4 = 0.037s$$

$$\text{Motor deceleration time } t_b = \frac{(Im + Il) \times n_1}{375 \times (Tm + Tl)} \times \frac{g}{1,000} \times 4$$

$$= \frac{(0.015 + 0.00130) \times 1,500}{375 \times (0.0895 + 0.02)} \times \frac{g}{1,000} \times 4 = 0.023s$$

Because t_b is smaller than t_s, the chain tension due to motor deceleration F_b is greater than that of the acceleration.

$$F_b = \frac{M \times V}{t_b \times 60 \times 1,000} + Fw = \frac{3,000 \times 6.2}{0.023 \times 60 \times 1,000} + 29.4 = 42.9 \text{ kN}$$

Therefore, the chain design tension:

$F'b = Fb \times Kv \times Kc \times Ku = 42.9 \times 1.02 \times 1.28 \times 0.6 = 33.6$ kN

When comparing the calculated chain tensions in Steps 2, 3, and 4, note that $F'b$ in Step 4 is the greatest. In this tension, Ku is already counted. Comparing $F'b$ with the maximum allowable tension of SUPER 120 chain, $F'b < 39.2$ kN. Therefore, this chain may be selected.

The example shown above is for chain in hanging drives. The maximum tension on the wrapping transmission chains is:

$F'b \times d / d' = 33.6 \times 171.22 / 303.75 = 18.9$ kN

This value is less than the maximum allowable tension of SUPER 100 chain, which is 30.4 kN. Therefore, this chain is acceptable.

Other Important Considerations

NOTE 1: If there are laws or regulations for chain selection, you must take them into account. For example, if the safety guideline says, "Safety factor must be greater than 10:1 compared with the minimum tensile strength," then you should design the equipment as shown above, and consider the following:

For hanging drive chain:

Minimum tensile strength

$= M \times g \times Ku \times 10 = 3,000 \times (9.80665 \times 10^{-3}) \times 0.6 \times 10 = 176.5$ kN

But the minimum tensile strength of SUPER 120 chain is only 124.6 kN, which is not enough to meet this requirement. Instead, select SUPER 140 chain (213 kN).

Wrapping transmission chain requires more than 99.5 kN of minimum tensile strength, therefore you may select SUPER 100 chain (111 kN).

Regulations are not always safer than manufacturer's suggested selection procedure. Choose the safest system possible.

NOTE 2: If a load greater than the motor braking torque very 48 occasionally occurs, the chains will be subjected to the following loads:

Wrapping transmission chain:

$$Fd = \frac{0.096 \times 1,000 \times 60 \times 2}{142.68} \times 0.6 = 48.4 \text{ kN}$$

Hanging drive chain:

$$48.4 \times \frac{303.75}{171.22} = 85.9 \text{ kN}$$

To avoid chain plastic deformation, the minimum tensile strength must be more than twice these loads (see Basics Section 2.1.1), therefore, you should select SUPER 100 chain and SUPER 160 chain.

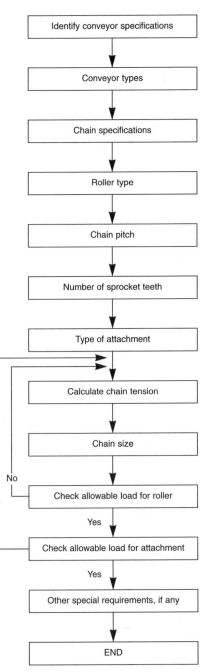

Figure 4.15 Chain Selection Procedure (Conveyor)

4.2 CONVEYOR CHAIN SELECTION

There are five types of conveyor chains:
- a. Small pitch conveyor chain.
- b. Precision conveyor chain.
- c. Top chain.
- d. Free flow chain.
- e. Large pitch conveyor chain.

To select any of these chains, use the procedure outlined in the flow chart (Figure 4.15). Chain tension is calculated based on the load size.

In these five types, because often the objects conveyed on small pitch conveyor chains, precision conveyor chains, and top chains are light, sometimes you don't have to check "allowable roller load." Also, attachments are not usually installed on top chains and free flow chains, therefore, you don't need to check the attachment allowable load.

4.2.1 Check of Conditions for Selection

You should check the items shown below:

1. Application conditions: application environment, indoor or outdoor, temperature, existence of foreign objects.
2. Conveyed objects: type (unit materials, bulk materials), abrasive, corrosive, temperature (high or low), dimension (for unit material), weight (unit material kg/unit; bulk material kg/m^3).
3. Maximum conveyance volume (unit materials, kg/conveyor length; bulk materials, tons/hour).
4. Method of conveyance: pushing with dog attachments, conveyed objects placed directly on the chains, etc.

5. Length of the conveyor, shaft center distance, vertical rise, general layout.
6. The chain speed (m/min.).
7. Number of the chain strands, interval length.
8. The chain pitch, attachment spacing and type.
9. The number of sprocket teeth, or pitch diameter.
10. Working hours (hours/day, hours/year).
11. Lubrication.
12. Motor: AC or DC, kW × number of motors.
13. Noise: If there is any noise constraint, use a larger number of sprocket teeth. Consult the manufacturer.

Some Additional Thoughts

You can make your decision on point 4 after reviewing the points in Basics Section 4.2.2, Conveyor Type Selection. Make sure to follow the procedure carefully.

Point 7 is more difficult to determine than it looks; the materials being conveyed impact the decision. Because the chain sizes and configuration may change as the design is developed, you must consider this point carefully. Consider these examples:

- If you convey fixed-sized pallets directly on chain, you usually need two sets of chains. But if the pallet is not rigid enough, you should include a third chain between the two outer chains.
- If you convey different-sized pipes or similar items directly on chain, you must consider the shortest length so that at least two chains are supporting the product on line, and determine the appropriate number of chains so that the chains are equally loaded.

Points 8, 9, and 12 may be revised as you proceed with the selection process since the chain sizes are usually determined by roller load, so make a preliminary selection first.

4.2.2 Conveyor Type Selection

According to conveyed object type (unit or bulk materials), typical chain conveyor types are sorted as shown on the next page. Therefore, you should choose the formation from among these.

In Figure 4.16, the available chain types are abbreviated below. These abbreviations mean:

RF: Double pitch roller chain, RF conveyor chain. Plastic roller and plastic sleeve chain may be used to convey unit materials.

RS: RS attachment chain

RF-B: RF bearing roller conveyor chain

RFN: Bearing bush chain

RFD: Deep link chain

VR: DOUBLE PLUS® chain

Conveyor Types	Material Conveyed			
	Unit	Type of Chain	Bulk	Type of Chain
Loading	Slat Conveyor 	RF-B RFN RF (CT)	Apron Conveyor 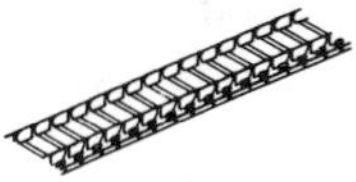	RF
	Pusher Conveyor, Tow Conveyor, Roller Coaster 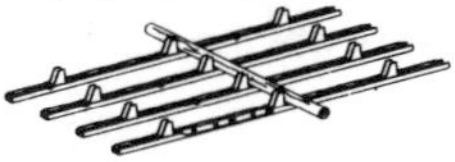	RF RFN NF RF-SR		
	Free Flow Conveyor 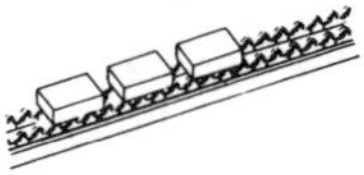	RF-VR RF-TR RF-SR		
	Plain Chain Conveyor 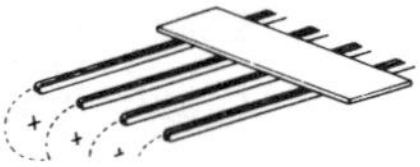	RF NF EPC RFD		
Elevating	Trolley Conveyor	RF	Bucket Elevator 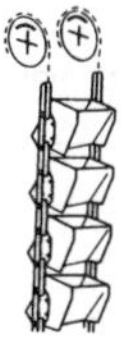	RF
	Tray Elevator 	RFN RF NF	Bucket-Type Continuous Unloader	Special Chain
	Tower Parking 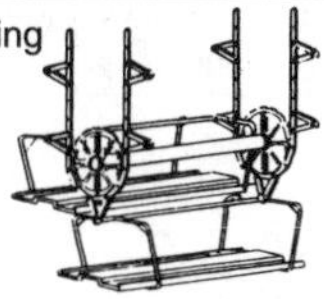	Special Chain		
Pushing or Conveying with Friction	Pusher Conveyor 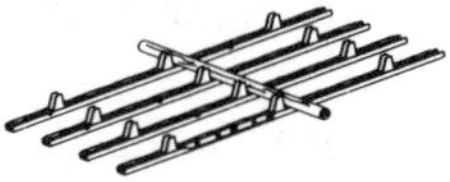	RF NF RFD	Scraper/Flight Conveyor 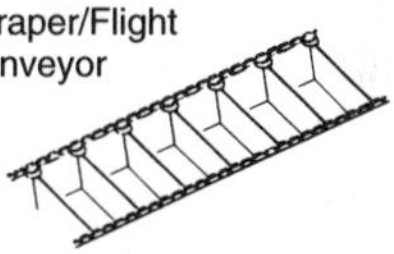	RF
	Horizontal Circulating Conveyor 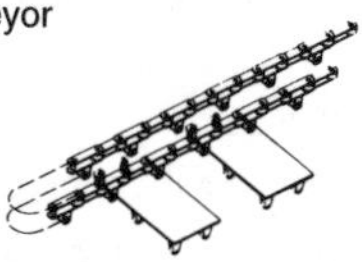	RF RFN	Flow Conveyor 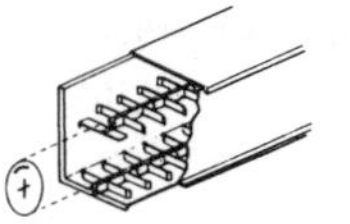	RF NFX

Figure 4.16   Types of Conveyor Chains

TR: Top roller chain
SR: Outboard roller chain
TP: Top chain
NF: Block chain (bar and pin)
NFX: Block chain—flow conveyor type
See Applications Section for details of these chains.

4.2.3 Selection of Chain Type and Specification

A conveyor design can use a variety of chains, depending on the type of operation, conditions, and material conveyed. Here we present a few points of notice about selection.

1. Consider RF, RS, or TP chain first. Typical applications are outlined in Table 4.4.
2. If there are no special temperature or environment concerns, and if the chain is not subject to rough usage, you can use plastic roller or RF-B chain. This reduces the amount of friction.
3. When you require accurate stopping location or must avoid chain elongation, select RFN.
4. NF is suitable for rough use and for conveyance of high-temperature objects.

Table 4.4 Determination by Usage

Type of Chain	Pitch	Roller Type	Center Distance	Conveyed Material		
				Weight	Size	Rigidity
RS Attachment Chain	Short	S	Short	Light	Small	Low
RF Double Pitch Chain	Medium	R • S	Medium	Light	Small ~ Medium	Mid
RF Conveyor Chain	Long	R• F • S	Long	Medium ~ Heavy	Medium ~ Large	High
Table Top Chain	Medium	N/A	Medium	Light	Small ~ Medium	Low

4.2.4 Points of Notice About Roller Type

Figure 4.17 shows the roller types and ways of guiding used in conveyor chains.

1. First of all, consider if an R-roller will meet the operating conditions.
2. An S-roller is designed to relieve shock caused by sprocket engagement, but when the conveyed objects are light and the conveyor length is short, an S-roller may be used.
3. An F-roller is used primarily to prevent snaking in large pitch conveyor chains. Because its flange operates and wears against the side rail, it is not the roller of choice to convey heavy objects or bulk material or to operate at high speeds.

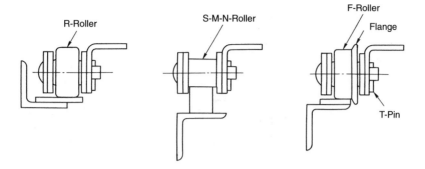

Figure 4.17 Conveyor Rollers and Guiding Mechanisms

4.2.5 Chain Pitch Decision

There is only one pitch for any given small pitch conveyor chain, double pitch roller chain, and RS attachment chain. Therefore, if you decide on the chain size according to strength, you must also determine the chain pitch at the same time. Chain pitch is measured in inches.

There are a couple of chain pitches for each size of large pitch RF conveyor chain. You must first choose the right size, then select the chain pitch. Large pitch chain is measured in millimeters.

The spacing of conveyed objects and the relationship between the sprocket diameter and amount of available space can impact the chain-pitch decision. For example, when pushing unit materials with a pusher at intervals of 2 m, you must select a chain pitch that is a multiple: 50, 100, 200, 250, 500 mm.

In general, here is how larger pitch chain compares to smaller pitch chain:
1. Larger pitch chain costs less.
2. Attachments on larger pitch chain are stronger.
3. Because of the decrease in the number of teeth in the sprockets, chordal action is greater.
4. Larger pitch chain systems tend to be noisier.
5. The pin and the bushings of larger pitch chain wear faster.

4.2.6 Deciding the Number of Sprocket Teeth

The number of sprocket teeth is limited by the chain pitch and the chain speed (Figure 4.18). If noise is a consideration, consult the manufacturer.

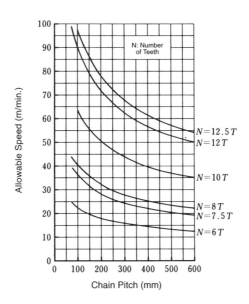

Figure 4.18 Chain Pitch Versus Allowable Speed

4.2.7 Deciding the Attachment Type

See the chapters on standard, Plus α Alpha, and special attachments in the Applications Section.

4.2.8 Calculation of Tension

Here we have an example to determine the tension in a horizontal conveyor and free flow conveyor.

Terms

T_{max}: Maximum chain tension (kN).

  T: Static chain tension at each part of conveyor (kN).

  Q: Maximum weight of conveyed objects (t/h).

  V: Conveying speed (the chain speed). (m/min.).

  H: Vertical center distance between sprockets (m).

  L: Horizontal center distance between sprockets (m).

  C: Center distance between sprockets (m).

  m: Mass of the working portion of the chain (kg/m). The mass of the chain × number of the chain strands, bucket, apron, etc.

M: Mass of the conveyed object in conveying section (kg/m).

f_1: Coefficient of friction between the chain and the guide rail when conveying.

f_2: Coefficient of friction between the chain and the conveyed objects in the accumulating section.

4.2.8.1 Horizontal Conveyor

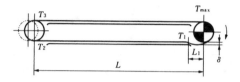

Horizontal Conveyor

$$T_1 = 1.35 \times m \times L_1 \times \frac{g}{1,000} \text{ (kN)}$$

$$T_2 = (L - L_1) \times m \times f_1 \times \frac{g}{1,000} + T_1 \text{ (kN)}$$

$$T_3 = 1.1 \times T_2 \text{ (kN)}$$

$$T_{max} = (M + m) \times L \times f_1 \times \frac{g}{1,000} + T_3 \text{ (kN)}$$

4.2.8.2 Free Flow Conveyor

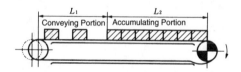

Free Flow Conveyor

$$T_{max} = 2.1 \times m \times (L_1 + L_2) \times f_1 \times \frac{g}{1,000} + M \times L_1 \times f_1$$

$$\times \frac{g}{1,000} + M_1 \times L_2 \times f_2 \times \frac{g}{1,000} \text{ (kN)}$$

L_1: Length of conveying portion (m).

L_2: Length of accumulating portion (m).

M_1: Weight of conveyed objects in accumulating portion (kg/m).

Table 4.5 shows the allowable carrying load for each size of large pitch conveyor chain when it is used in horizontal conveyance.

Table 4.5 Allowable Conveyed Loads for Selected Conveyor Chains

units: kg/strand of chain

Conveyor Chain Size	Allowable Conveyed Load	
	RF Conveyor Chain	Bearing Roller Chain
RF03	5,400	14,000
RF05	12,500	33,300
RF08 • 450	14,300	36,700
RF10	20,500	53,300
RF12	33,900	90,000
RF17	44,600	116,700
RF26	57,100	150,000
RF36	86,600	230,000
RF60	91,100	-
RF90	143,800	-
RF120	201,800	-

NOTE: Calculated for horizontal conveyor. Safety factor = 7; Coefficient of rolling friction for RF type = 0.08, for bearing roller type = 0.03

4.2.9 Allowable Load of Roller and Standard A Attachment

There are two kinds of allowable roller load: one is caused by load weight (Figure 4.21); the other by corner rail (Figure 4.22).

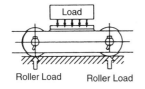

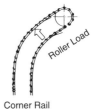

Figure 4.21	Allowable Load Caused by Load Weight

Figure 4.22	Allowable Load Caused by Corner Rail

Each manufacturer's catalog shows the allowable roller load, according to each roller type and design. Check the appropriate catalogs.

NOTE: The values listed for bearing roller chain and plastic roller chain are for unlubricated operation; the values for other types of chain are for lubricated conditions.

On the standard A attachment, bending load occurs from the carried load. Twisting forces may also occur, depending on the direction of the load. The manufacturer's catalog shows the allowable load for bending load.

4.3 SELECTION EXAMPLE

Now that we've covered the procedures you need to follow to choose a conveyor chain, let's complete an example.

Your assignment: Select a suitable chain for the conditions shown in Figure 4.23.

1. Operating conditions (Figure 4.23). In addition, note the following:
   - The conveyed object is steel pipe supported on a plate.
   - The system operates in a clean environment.
   - The environment and conveyed objects are at ambient temperature.
   - The chain can be lubricated.
2. The chain conveyor type: loading on slat conveyor.
3. The chain type: check both RF and RF-B types.
4. The roller type: R-roller.
5. The chain pitch: 250 mm.
6. The number of sprocket teeth: based on the chain pitch and the chain speed, select six teeth.
7. The attachment type: A-2.
8. Determine the chain size from the tension.

In this example, two sets of chain convey 80,000 kg. Therefore, each of the selected chains must be able to carry more than 40,000 kg per one set.

Table 4.5 shows you that either RF17 (general series) or RF10-B are acceptable.

NOTE: We are ignoring the dynamic tension of starting and stopping to make the example easier to understand.

9. The allowable roller load.

Chain pitch is 250 mm and the length of the conveyed object is 1,000 mm. Object length /pitch = the number of rollers under the conveyed object. 1,000 /250 = 4 rollers

If we use two sets of chain, there are eight rollers under one conveyed object. If the steel pipes on the plate are not carried equally, uneven load occurs on the roller. In this process, we presume that only four rollers share the load.

The roller's load = (2,000 × g) / 4 = 4,900 N = 4.9 kN

According to the catalog, either RF26 (standard series) or RF12-B (roller bearing) may be selected.

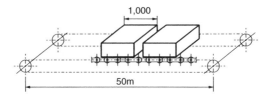

Double Strand Conveyor
Conveyor Length: 50m   Chain Speed: 10m/min.
Weight of Conveyed Material: 2,000kg/pc x 40pcs
Chain: P=250mm   R–Roller   A-2 Attachment

Figure 4.23   Parameters for Example Selection Process

10. The allowable load of standard A attachment.
    There are eight A attachments under each pallet. Assume that four
    attachments receive the load equally. The load on the A attachments
    = 4,900 N. According to the catalogs, RF12 (basic series) or stronger
    is acceptable.
11. Taking into account the tension, the allowable roller load, and the
    allowable load for standard A attachments, RF26250-R (general series)
    or RF12250-BR (roller bearing) may be selected.
12. Motor size.

$$\text{Motor (kW)} = \frac{T \times V}{54.5} \times \frac{1}{\eta} \quad (\eta = 0.85 \text{ motor efficiency})$$

When using bearing roller conveyor chain, $f_1 = 0.03$.

$$T = 2{,}000 \text{ kg} \times \frac{g}{1{,}000} \times 40 \text{ pieces} \times 0.03 = 23.5 \text{ kN } \{2{,}400 \text{ kgf}\}$$

$$\text{kW} = \frac{23.5 \times 10}{54.5} \times \frac{1}{0.85} = 5.1 \text{ kW}$$

When using RF series conveyor chain, $f_1 = 0.08$.

$$T = 2{,}000 \text{ kg} \times \frac{g}{1{,}000} \times 40 \text{ pieces} \times 0.08 = 62.8 \text{ kN } \{6{,}400 \text{ kgf}\}$$

$$\text{kW} = \frac{62.8 \times 10}{54.5} \times \frac{1}{0.85} = 13.6 \text{ kW}$$

The process is straightforward and logical. And you can see that a bearing roller conveyor chain, because it has lower friction, allows you to use a
smaller chain and a smaller motor.

5. CHAINS AND ENVIRONMENTS

Most chain is made of metal or engineered plastic, which may be impacted by the conditions under which the chain is operated. For example, the temperature or the amount of dust in the air can affect the chain. When you select a chain for your application, you have to take into account the environment in which the chain is operated.

In this chapter, we will explain problems that may develop when operating a chain under certain conditions, and how to deal with them.

5.1 STEEL CHAINS

5.1.1 Use of Steel Chains in High Temperatures

When heat-treated chains are run in temperatures higher than their tempering limits, the following problems may occur:

- Increased wear due to decreased hardness.
- Improper lubrication due to lubricant deterioration or carbonization.
- Stiff joints and increased wear due to oxide scale formation.
- Decrease in strength.

To prevent lubricant deterioration at high temperatures, use a special lubricant. Table 5.1 shows the transmission capability of power transmission roller chains with high-temperature lubricant. Check the manufacturer's catalog for additional information.

When chains are used in temperatures above 250°C, pay special attention to the composition and heat-treatment of the chain. The most popular type of chain for high temperature is SS specification, which is made of 304 stainless steel, and has a maximum working temperature of 650°C at low speeds. However, to maintain an adequate safety margin at a high temperature like this, we suggest you use NS-specification chain. NS chain is made of 316 stainless steel, which contains molybdenum and less carbon. NS specification has worked at low speed in environments up to 700°C.

If your operation runs at temperatures higher than 400°C, consult the manufacturer before making your chain selection. Production methods and materials may be specially adapted for your application.

Table 5.1 Transmission Capabilities with High-Temperature Lubricants

Operating Temperature	Calculation[1]
Up to 150°C	MAX
150°C to 200°C	MAX x 3/4
200°C to 250°C	MAX x 1/2
Over 250°C	Out of Use

[1] MAX = Maximum allowable load as shown in the manufacturer's catalog

5.1.2 Use of Steel Chains in Low Temperatures

When you use chains in low temperatures, the following problems may occur:

- Decrease in shock strength due to low-temperature brittleness.
- Lubricant solidification.
- Stiff joints caused by frost or ice.

Table 5.2 shows the power transmission capacity of drive chains at low temperatures.

Table 5.2 Transmission Capabilities of Chains at Low Temperatures

Operating Temperature	Standard Roller Chain (RS80)[1]	KT Type[1]
Below -60°C	Out of use	Out of use
-60°C to -50°C	Out of use	MAX x 1/2
-50°C to -40°C	Out of use	MAX x 2/3
-40°C to -30°C	MAX x 1/4	MAX
-30°C to -20°C	MAX x 1/3	MAX
-20°C to -10°C	MAX x 1/2	MAX
-10°C to +60°C	MAX	MAX

[1] MAX = Maximum allowable load as shown in the manufacturer's catalog

Two types of chain are especially useful at lower temperatures. KT-specification chain is specially heat-treated to withstand very cold environments. SS-specification chain, which is made of 304 stainless steel, may also be used at low temperatures. Low-temperature brittleness does not occur in austenitic stainless steel.

These chains cannot fix the problems of solidification of the lubricant or stiff joints caused by frost or ice. Use cold-temperature oil or grease and apply it to the inner clearances and the outside of the chain.

5.2 ENGINEERED PLASTIC CHAIN IN HIGH AND LOW TEMPERATURES

Standard engineered plastic chain can be run at temperatures between -20°C and 80°C. At higher temperatures, it may become soft and not keep its shape; at lower temperatures it may become brittle.

KV-specification super engineered plastic chain may be used for continuous driving up to 250°C. Consult the manufacturer regarding KV specification, because the available chain types and sizes are limited.

5.3 OTHER CHAIN MATERIALS IN HIGH TEMPERATURES

At very high temperatures, engineered ceramic is the material of choice. It offers extreme heat resistance. It has endured repeated temperature changes from ambient up to 1,200°C (Figure 5.1).

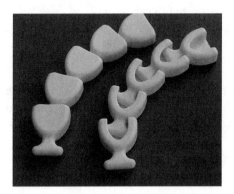

Figure 5.1   Engineered Ceramic Chain Will Endure Very High Temperatures

5.4 COPING WITH SPECIAL CONDITIONS

When you use a metal or engineered plastic chain in special conditions, other environmental factors need to be considered. For example, if the chain gets wet, the wear life may change. Please refer to the sections shown below.

5.4.1 Use in Wet Conditions

When metal chains are splashed with water or go through heated vapor, the following problems may occur:

* Increase in wear due to improper or insufficient lubrication.
* Decrease in strength due to corrosive attack.
* Shortened chain life due to rust or corrosion of the chain.

You can take the following steps to reduce the effect of wet conditions in several ways:

1. Use larger-sized chains to decrease the bearing pressure and increase wear resistance.
2. Allow for the corrosive-reduction factor in your calculations.
3. Use plated steel or stainless steel chain.

Wear of engineered plastic chains may increase if they are used in water. In wet applications, stainless steel chains will wear less than engineered plastic chains.

5.4.2 Use in Acidic, Alkaline, or Electrolytic Conditions

If chain is exposed to sulfuric acid or nitric acid, the following problems may occur:

- Increase in wear due to chemical corrosion beyond normal mechanical wear.
- Brittle failure of chain parts (especially plates).
- Decrease in strength due to corrosion.
- Shortened chain fatigue life due to oxidization or corrosion.

A chain exposed to an electrolytic liquid, such as sea or mine water, may develop pitting corrosion, electrocorrosion, or electrochemical corrosion. There are chains that resist these types of corrosion. Table 5.3 shows examples of typical corrosion resistance of each chain type. In general, the corrosiveness changes based on the strength and temperature of the liquid. Use the information in Table 5.3 only as a reference. Select chains after thorough testing.

5.4.3 Use in Abrasive Conditions

Strong abrasive materials, such as sand, coke, metal particles, or substantial amounts of dust in the air may affect the wear life of a chain. The particles may get into the chain's working parts and engaging parts between the chain and the sprockets. In this case, you can take these steps:

1. Select a chain with hardened working parts. The parts need to be harder than the foreign objects.
2. Reduce the bearing pressure by using a larger-sized chain. This increases the abrasion-wear area.

If you're operating conveyor chains in abrasive conditions, consider the following points:

1. Select a chain with thicker bushings to increase the abrasion-wear area.
2. Design the system so that the plates slide on the rails rather than roll on them. The bottom edge of the plate may accept much more abrasion wear than the area between the bushings and the rollers.
3. Install many small rollers in the equipment, instead of rails. This is especially useful when conveying objects that cause significant wear.

In addition to causing wear, some objects may get into the working clearances of the chain, making it difficult or impossible for the chain to bend or rotate. In such cases, take the following steps:

1. Use seals, such as oil seal, labyrinth seal, or O-ring seals, to prevent particles from getting into the chain. (Applicable size is limited.)
2. Install a grease nipple and grease the chain regularly. Grease will force the particles from the chain. (Applicable size is limited.)
3. Increase the clearances so that particles will fall out, even if they get into the chain. This is the most common method.

Table 5.3. Resistance to Corrosive Agents

Corrosive Agent	Conc.	Temp. (°C)	Anti-corrosive Roller Chain							Sprockets	
			SS	AS	CS	NS	TI	PC	PC•SY	Engineered Plastic	304SS
Acetone		20	1	1	1	1	1	1	4	1	1
Oil (Vegetable, Mineral)		20	1	1	1	1	1	1	1	1	1
Linseed Oil	100%	20	1	2	2	1	1	1	3	1	1
Sulfurous Acid Gas		20	1	4	4	1	1	3	3	3	1
Alcohol		20	1	1	1	1	1	1	1	1	1
Ammonia (Aqueous)		20	1	1	1	1	1	1	1	1	1
Whiskey		20	1	1	1	1	1	1	1	1	1
Ethyl Ether		20	1	1	1	1	1	1	1	1	1
Zinc Chloride	50%	20	2	4	4	2	1	2	1	4	2
Ammonium Chloride	50%	Boiling	2	4	4	1	1	3	3	3	2
Potassium Chloride	Saturated	20	1	2	2	1	1	3	3	1	1
Calcium Chloride	Saturated	20	2	4	4	1	1	2	1	1	2
Ferric Chloride	5%	20	2	4	4	2	1	3	3	4	2
Sodium Chloride	5%	20	1	2	2	1	1	1	1	1	1
Hydrochloric Acid	2%	20	4	4	4	4	1	4	1	4	4
Chlorine Gas (Dry)		20	2	4	4	2	1	3	1	4	2
Chlorine Gas (Wet)		20	4	4	4	2	1	3	1	4	4
Chlorine Water		20	4	4	4	1	1	4	3	4	4
Oleic Acid		20	1	1	1	1	1	1	3	1	1
Sea Water		20	2	4	4	1	1	2	1	1	2
Sodium Perchlorate	10%	Boiling	1	4	4	1	1	3	3	3	1
Hydrogen Peroxide	30%	20	1	2	2	1	1	4	1	4	1
Gasoline		20	1	1	1	1	1	1	1	1	1
Potassium Nitrate	25%	20	1	1	1	1	1	1	3	1	1
Potassium Nitrate	25%	Boiling	1	4	4	1	1	3	3	3	1
Vinegar		20	2	4	4	1	1	2	1	2	2
Potassium Hydroxide	20%	20	1	1	1	1	1	1	1	1	1
Calcium Hydroxide	20%	Boiling	1	1	1	1	1	1	1	3	1
Sodium Hydroxide	25%	20	1	1	1	1	1	1	1	1	1
Stearic Acid	100%	Boiling	4	4	4	1	1	4	3	1	4
Beverage			1	1	1	1	1	1	1	1	1
Carbolic Acid		20	1	1	1	1	1	4	1	4	1
Petroleum		20	1	1	1	1	1	1	3	1	1
Water (Soapy)		20	1	1	1	1	1	1	1	1	1
Soda Water			1	1	1	1	1	3	3	3	1
Sodium Hydrogen		20	1	1	1	1	1	1	3	1	1
Sodium Carbonate	Saturated	Boiling	1	1	1	1	1	3	1	2	1
Sodium Thiosulfate	25%	Boiling	1	1	1	1	1	3	3	3	1
Turpentine		35	1	1	1	1	1	3	3	3	1
Kerosene		20	1	1	1	1	1	3	1	3	1
Varnish			1	1	1	1	1	3	3	3	1
Nitric Acid	65%	20	1	4	4	1	1	4	1	4	1
Nitric Acid	65%	Boiling	2	4	4	2	1	4	4	4	2
Lactic Acid	10%	20	1	2	2	1	1	3	3	1	1
Honey			1	1	1	1	1	1	1	1	1
Paraffin		20	1	1	1	1	1	1	1	1	1

1 = High corrosion resistance
2 = Partial corrosion resistance
3 = Unknown
4 = Not resistant

Bearing roller chain and bearing bush chain contain rotating elements, so they are very sensitive to particulate contamination. Make sure you install fixed seals when operating either of these.

6. BASIC LAYOUTS

To achieve the maximum benefit from a chain drive, it is important to arrange chains and sprockets properly. In the following section, we will explain some examples.

6.1 BASIC LAYOUTS OF WRAPPING TRANSMISSION CHAINS

6.1.1 General Arrangements

When designing the wrapping transmission drive, the center line of both sprockets should be close to horizontal. The angle of inclination may be up to 60°. The slack should be on the lower side.

The center distance of the sprockets should be 30 to 50 times the pitch of the chain. When the chain is subjected to fluctuating load, the center distance of the sprockets should be less than 20 times the chain pitch. This is shown in Figure 6.1.

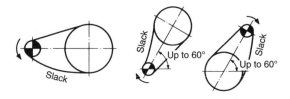

Figure 6.1   Drive Positions

6.1.2 Special Layouts

1. Slack side on top (Figures 6.2 and 6.3)

If the shaft center distance is short, proper chain tension should be maintained by adjusting the shaft center distance.

If the shaft center distance is long, do not allow the two sides of the chain to touch each other. Reduce slack span by installing an idler.

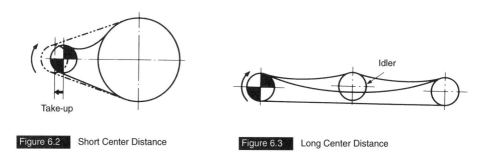

Figure 6.2 Short Center Distance

Figure 6.3 Long Center Distance

2. High chain speed and fluctuating loads

In this case, the chain's characteristic frequency, impact period of the driven shaft, or polygonal action created by the chain/sprocket engagement, may create large chain vibrations. A guide shoe made of NBR rubber or UHMW polyethylene will help reduce vibrations.

3. Vertical or near-vertical shaft centers

Install an automatic tensioner to eliminate excess chain slack. This is imperative if the driving shaft is on the bottom (Figure 6.4).

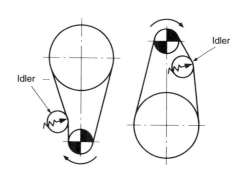

Figure 6.4 Vertical Drive

6.1.3 Special Arrangements

Chains may be arranged as shown in Figure 6.5 to transmit power. Check the manufacturer's specific suggestions on special layouts.

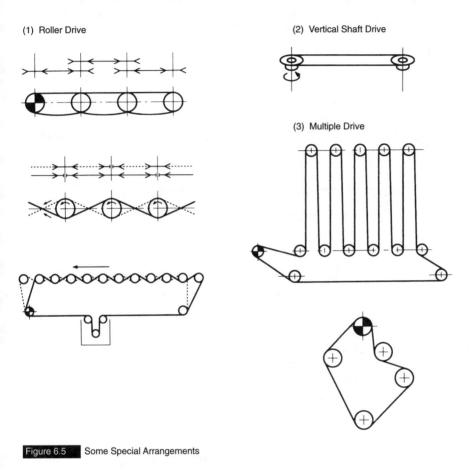

(1) Roller Drive

(2) Vertical Shaft Drive

(3) Multiple Drive

Figure 6.5   Some Special Arrangements

6.2 BASIC CONVEYOR CHAIN LAYOUTS

6.2.1 Horizontal Conveyor Arrangement

1. Guide rail arrangement

Chain slack may be eliminated by supporting the entire return side with a guide rail and installing a take-up on the driven shaft. The typical arrangement is shown in Figure 6.6 (1). This arrangement can be adapted for reversing drives.

2. Guide rail with catenary arrangement

Support the return chain side, in part, and have a catenary section as shown in Figures 6.6 (2) through (5). There are many advantages to this arrangement. The guide rail with catenary makes it easier to manage excessive chain (caused by temperature or abrasion) and to maintain proper tension. This arrangement is applicable to low-speed drives. The amount of sag should be 10 percent of the span. It is not appropriate for conveyors with reversing drives.

3. Bottomside conveying arrangement

The return side is on top in this arrangement. It is possible to make the return side act as the catenary take-up. Caution must be exercised so that the two sides of the chain don't touch each other.

Take-Up

(1) Return Side with Guide Rail Support and Take-Up on Driven Shaft

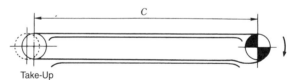

Take-Up

(2) Return Side with Catenary Section and Partial Guide Rail Support

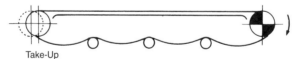

Take-Up

(3) Return Side with Catenary Roller Section

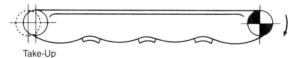

Take-Up

(4) Return Side with Catenary Guide Section Support

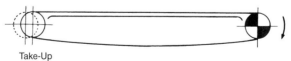

Take-Up

(5) Return Side with Catenary Section

Figure 6.6 Horizontal Conveyor Arrangements

6.2.2 Vertical Conveyor Arrangement

Install a brake or anti-reverse clutch on the driver in case the machine stops while conveying objects. This is shown in Figure 6.7.

The chain may vibrate considerably due to the characteristic frequency of the chain, impact period of the driven shaft, or the polygonal action of the chain and sprocket. Therefore, install a guide shoe to prevent vibration.

6.2.3 Inclined Conveyor Arrangement

An inclined conveyor is set up the same way as a horizontal conveyor.

6.2.4 Horizontal Circulating Conveyor Arrangement

If the shafts are vertical (Figure 6.8), install a guide roller or guide shoe to the chain to keep the chain from hanging down. This method is covered in more detail in the Applications Section of this book.

> *NOTE: For all conveyors, the use of a take-up is suggested. Take care not to overtension the chain, or the result will be increased wear between the pin and bushing. Also, if there is a corner roller guide, bushing/roller wear will occur. There must be adequate take-up allowance.*

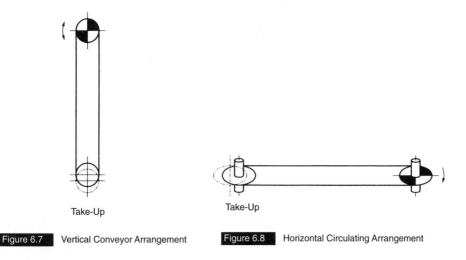

Take-Up	Take-Up

| Figure 6.7 | Vertical Conveyor Arrangement | Figure 6.8 | Horizontal Circulating Arrangement |

6.3 SUPPORTING THE ROLLER OF A CONVEYOR CHAIN

Support both the conveying side and the return side of the chain vertically and restrain them horizontally. Figure 6.9 shows examples of supporting each type of roller and attachment.

Basics

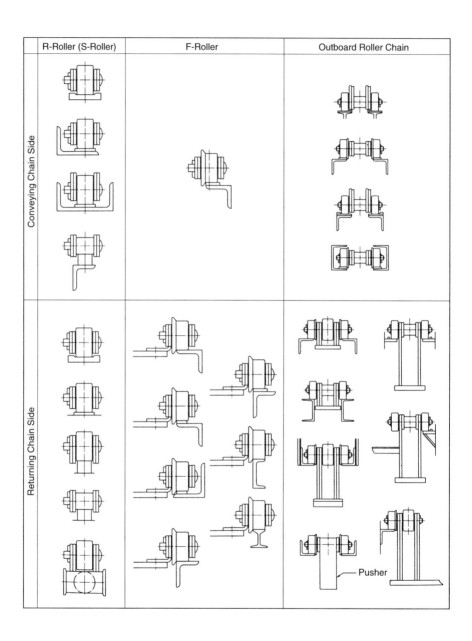

	R-Roller (S-Roller)	F-Roller	Outboard Roller Chain
Conveying Chain Side			
Returning Chain Side			Pusher

Figure 6.9   Supporting the Roller of a Conveyor Chain

68

7. MANIPULATION OF CHAINS

You've made your selection, ordered the chain, and it arrives. Now what? In this chapter, we will review how to get started. Specifically, we will discuss installing chain on the equipment; checking the accuracy of the installation; and testing, inspecting, and lubricating for start-up.

The guidelines in this chapter will get you started, but refer to your specific manufacturer's catalog for details.

7.1 TRANSMISSION CHAINS, SMALL PITCH CONVEYOR CHAINS

7.1.1 Installation

Most transmission chains are sold in standard lengths, usually 3,048 mm (10 ft). The length may vary, depending on the size of the chain. Small pitch conveyor chains may be special ordered in lengths of chain as required.

The first thing you must do is cut the chain to the length you need.

Tools: Angle grinder (to cut the riveted parts), chain vise, punch, hammer, chain screw.

Method

Step 1. Grind the riveted portion of the two pins with the angle grinder. If the chain has cottered pins, remove them.

Step 2. Secure the chain in the chain vise. Using the primary punch and the secondary punch (or the chain screw), remove one set of pins.

Step 3. Install both ends of the chain onto sprockets and join with connecting links (Figure 7.1). Be sure to install the clips or cotter pins as shown in Figures 7.2 and 7.3.

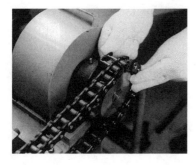

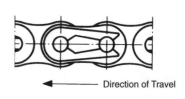

Direction of Travel

| Figure 7.1 | Installing a Chain | Figure 7.2 | Direction in which the Clip is Installed |

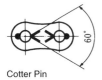
Cotter Pin

T-pin

Z-pin

Figure 7.3   Angle of Legs for Cotter Pins

7.1.2 Installation Accuracy

After installing the chain, you need to check the accuracy of the installation. This involves verifying the amount of slack and the precise positioning of the shafts.

7.1.2.1 Chain Slack

The chain slack that you can move by hand (length SS', see Figure 7.4) should be about 4 percent of the span (length A-B) unless one or more of the following conditions apply:

- The center line of sprockets is vertical or almost vertical.
- The center distance of sprockets is more than 1 m.
- The chain is subjected to heavy loads and frequent starts.
- The chain is subjected to suddenly reversing loads.

If one or more of these conditions apply to your operation, make the chain slack (length SS') about 2 percent.

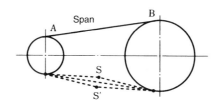

Figure 7.4   Chain Slack

7.1.2.2 Horizontal Precision and Parallelism of the Shafts

Position of the shafts is shown in Figure 7.5, Figure 7.6, and Figure 7.7.
1. Check the horizontal specification with a level. The shafts should be horizontal within ±1/300.
2. Check the parallelism with a scale. They should be within (length A – B) / L = ±1/300.
3. Align the sprocket faces within tolerances shown in the table (Figure 7.7).

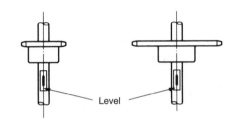

Figure 7.5   Horizontal Positioning of the Shafts

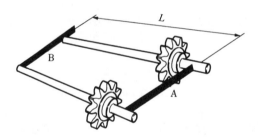

Figure 7.6   Parallelism of the Shafts

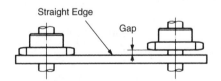

Figure 7.7   Alignment of Sprockets

Distance between Shafts	Gap
Up to 1 m	± 1 mm
1 m to 10 m	± $\dfrac{\text{Distance between Shafts (mm)}}{1,000}$
Over 10 m	± 10 mm

7.1.3 Start-Up

7.1.3.1 Prestart-Up Checklist

Before you start running the chain, check the following:
1. Connecting plates, clips, and cotter pins are installed correctly.
2. The chain slack has been properly adjusted.
3. Adequate lubrication is available.
4. The chain doesn't touch any objects, like chain cases, etc.
5. There are no objects in the chain area, and all is clean.

7.1.3.2 Start-Up Test

Before beginning full operation, turn on the power and check the following:
1. Sound. There should be no strange noises. Make sure the chain doesn't touch the case.
2. Vibration. Look for excessive chain vibration.
3. Sprocket-chain interaction. Make sure the chain doesn't climb over the sprockets.
4. Sprockets. Be sure the chain separates smoothly from the sprocket.
5. Chain articulation. The chain should be articulating smoothly.

If you notice any of these conditions, do not begin operation. Equipment or chain could be damaged. Correct any problems before proceeding. (See Basics Section 7.1.6 for additional information.)

7.1.4 Lubrication

Power transmission chains and small pitch conveyor chains are usually pre-lubricated with rust-prevention oil before shipping. Nevertheless, it is essential to lubricate roller chain. Properly lubricated chain has a longer wear life and is less likely to develop rust.

Lubricate the chain where the tension is minimal, applying the lubricant in the clearance between the link plates (Figure 7.8).

Figure 7.9 shows the lubrication method and type of oil. Table 7.1 shows suggested lubricants for low-speed operation. If your operation runs at high speeds or in very high or low temperatures, refer to the manufacturer's catalog for information on proper lubrication.

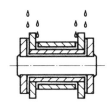

Figure 7.8 Lubricate Chain in the Clearance Between Link Plates

Table 7.1 Suggested Lubricants

Chain No.	Ambient Temperature Range			
	-10°C ~ 0°C	0°C ~ 40°C	40°C ~ 50°C	50°C ~ 60°C
RS50 and smaller	SAE10W	SAE20	SAE30	SAE40
RS60 • RS80	SAE20	SAE30	SAE40	SAE50
RS100	SAE20	SAE30	SAE40	SAE50
RS120 and larger	SAE30	SAE40	SAE50	SAE50

	Method	Quantity of Oil
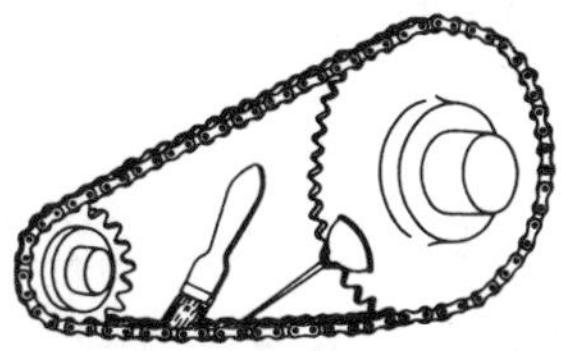	Manual Application. Oil is applied with an oil filler or brush on the slack side of the chain.	Oil should be applied at fixed intervals, usually about every eight hours, or as often as necessary to prevent the bearing areas from becoming dry.
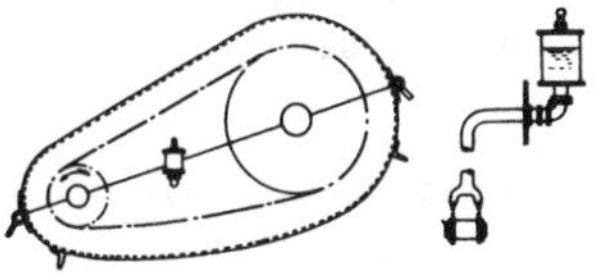	Drip Lubrication. A simple case can be used. Oil from the oil cup is supplied by drip feeding.	Apply 5 to 20 drops of oil per minute for every strand of chain. Actual quantity depends on the speed.
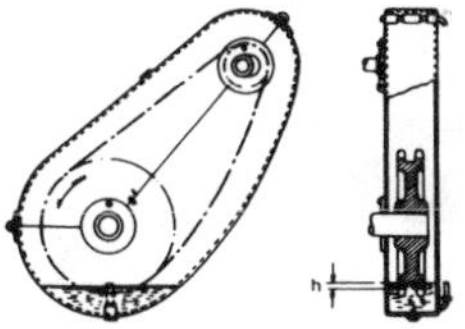	Oil Bath Lubrication. The chain is installed in a leak-free casing.	Chain should be submerged in oil 6 mm to 12 mm. If h is too large, the composition of the oil may change due to heat generated and lose some of its effectiveness.

Figure 7.9 Proper Lubrication Methods

7.1.5 Inspection

Chains are reliable components of a transmission machine. If you selected the proper chain and use it within its specified conditions, the chain will last for a long time.

However, you must perform regular inspections on the chain to make sure it is in good condition and operating correctly. Perform inspections monthly or more often if the chain is used in harsh environments. Why are inspections important? Over the life of a chain, the pins and bushings wear gradually. There may have been an unexpected shock load on the line, or a malfunctioning oven might expose the chain to very hot conditions.

During an inspection, make sure to check for the following conditions:
- Cracks in the link plates (Figure 7.10).
- Cracks in the rollers (Figure 7.11).
- Rotated pins (Figure 7.12).
- Wear on the end surfaces of link plates (Figure 7.13).

If you find any of these conditions, take immediate steps to correct the problem. A quick checklist is included in Table 7.2. In addition, some troubleshooting tips are included in Section 7.1.6.

Table 7.2 Inspection Checklist

Procedure	Inspection
1. Visually check the chain during operation.	In addition to the items to check during operation given in Section 7.1.3, also confirm that the lubrication conditions are suitable. (Look at both the method and amount of lubrication.)
2. Stop the chain and carefully inspect each part of the chain and sprocket.	1. Check the external cleanliness, corrosive, and lubrication conditions; also look for scratches or other damage to the link plate side and edge surfaces, pin edges, and roller surfaces. 2. Inspect for pin rotation and the gap between the plate and the pins. 3. Inspect the sprocket teeth surfaces and teeth side surfaces for scratches or marks. 4. Measure the elongation of the chain due to wear. 5. Check the flex of the chain and the spin of the rollers. 6. When using a terminating device for lift applications, inspect the wear of the terminator and the wear of the pins. Also, check for proper installation.

Positions Where Cracks are Likely to Develop

Figure 7.10 Example of a Crack on a Link Plate   **Figure 7.11** Cracks on the Rollers

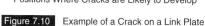

Correct Position   Rotated Position   H   5% of H

Figure 7.12 Rotation of the Pins   **Figure 7.13** Wear on the End Surfaces of the Plates

7.1.6 Troubleshooting and Problem-Solving

If you find something wrong with a chain during start-up or regular inspection, it may require treatment or you may need to replace it with a new chain. A variety of problems and their solutions is shown in Figure 7.14.

Symptom	Possible Causes	Remedy
Chain is riding up on the sprocket. 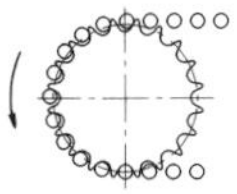	The chain and sprocket do not match.	Replace the chain or sprocket with the correct size.
	Excessive load.	Decrease the load, or increase the number of strands or size of the chain.
	Elongation of the chain due to chain wear or excessively worn sprocket teeth.	Replace with new chain and sprockets.
Unusual noises.	Improper installation of the sprocket or axle.	Inspect and correct.
	Chain casing or bearings are loose.	Tighten all bolts and nuts.
	Excessive or insufficient slack in the chain.	Adjust the distance between axles to obtain the proper amount of slack.
	Excessively worn chain or sprocket.	Replace the chain and sprocket with new chain and sprocket.
	Not enough lubrication.	Provide proper lubrication according to the operating conditions.

Excessive vibrations in chain.	Chain is resonating with a periodic external force. 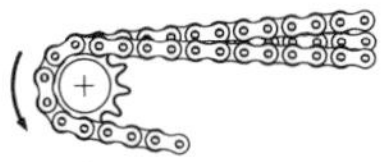	Change the chain's mode of vibration.
		1. Preventing resonance.
		  a. To change the natural frequency of the chain.
		    • Alter the effective tension either by applying an initial tension or adjusting the existing one.
		    • Install a tensioner to change the chain span.
		    • Replace the chain. Choose a different quality and spring coefficient.
		  b. Change the vibration frequency.
		    • Change the speed of rotation of the sprocket.
		    • Re-evaluate the device set-up.
		2. Mechanically reducing the vibrations.
		    • Install a guide shoe.
		    • Install a self-adjusting tensioner on the slack side. 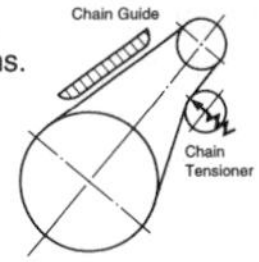

	Load fluctuations are excessively large.	Reduce fluctuations with fluid coupling or similar technique.
The chain winds onto the sprocket (poor separation from the sprocket teeth). 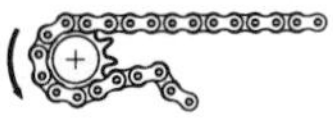	Span between axles is too large.	Install an idler.
	Excessive slack in chain.	Adjust the chain length or distance between axles. Install a tensioner.
	Elongation of the chain due to chain wear or excessively worn sprocket teeth.	Replace with new chain and sprocket.
Rusting of the chain.	Improper lubrication or poor environment.	Replace chain and protect it from the environment with chain casing or proper lubrication.
Excessive wear at the inside surface of link plates and sides of sprocket teeth.	Improper installation. 	Correct sprocket and axle installation.
Excessive wear at the link plate side surfaces and pin heads.	Improper installation of guides, etc. 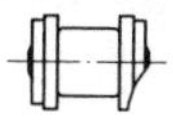	Check the condition of the guides, and increase the gap between the guides and chain.

Figure 7.14 (i)   Troubleshooting Chain Symptoms and Remedies
Transmission Chain, Small Conveyor Chain

Basics

Symptom	Possible Causes	Remedy
Improper flex or bending of chain, tight joints.	Chain is not installed correctly.	Inspect the installation and correct as necessary.
	Contamination from metal dust or dirt because of improper lubrication.	Remove the chain, wash it thoroughly, and provide proper lubrication.
	Excessive load or bent pin.	Reduce the load or increase the number of or size of chains. Replace chain with a larger size.
	Corrosion or rusting.	Install a chain casing to protect the chain.
	Seizing from improper lubrication.	Provide proper lubrication according to the operating conditions.
	Seizing of pin and bushing. Pin and bushing seized from high-speed operation. This causes improper bending and can lead to chain breakage. 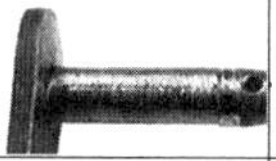	Provide the proper operating conditions.
Spreading of link plates.	Uneven or excessive loading caused by improper installation. 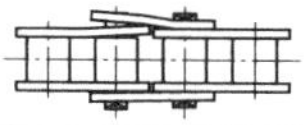	Replace with new chain and correct installation.

Figure 7.14 (i) Transmission Chain, Small Conveyor Chain (Cont.)

Symptom	Possible Causes	Remedy
Breakage of link plate.	Excessively large shock load.	Reduce shock loads by making the start-up, stopping, and other actions smoother (installing a shock absorber, etc.). Increase the size or number of chains.
	Vibrations in the chain.	Install an anti-vibration device (for example, tensioner or idler). Refer to "Excessive vibration in chain."
	Large inertia in the driven machine (excessive load).	Increase the size or number of chains.
	Corrosion.	Replace with a new chain. Install a casing to protect the chain. Otherwise, periodically clean the chain.

Figure 7.14 (ii) Link Plate

Symptom	Possible Causes	Remedy
(1) Static fracture. Stretching the link plate with a tensile load beyond its breaking load will cause it to stretch and then break.	(2) Fatigue fracture. By repeatedly applying a load past its fatigue limit (fatigue strength), the fatigue will start at holes and then suddenly break.	(3) Offset plate fatigue. Offset plates are bent at the center, and the resulting concentration of stress at the bend can cause a fatigue break. Avoid using offset links in high-stress applications.
Cracks in the link plates (fatigue), which are perpendicular to the direction of pull.	Loads are greater than allowable.	Remove all large or excessively repeating loads. Otherwise, increase the size or number of chains. Replace with a new chain.
Deformation in the link plate holes.	Excessive load.	Remove the cause of the excessive load. Replace with a new chain.
Corrosion stress cracks appear, usually as bow-shaped cracks in the link plate.	The chain is being used in an acidic or alkaline environment. (This is not caused by a repetitive load.)	Install a casing to protect the chain from the environment. Consider a chain with a high resistance to corrosion stress cracks. Replace with a new chain.

Figure 7.14 (ii) Link Plate (Cont.)

Symptom	Possible Causes	Remedy
Breakage of pin.	Excessively large shock load.	Reduce shock loads by making the start-up, stopping, and other actions smoother.
	Subject to a repetitive load greater than the fatigue limit of the pin.	Remove the large repetitive load. Otherwise, increase the size or number of chains.
	Corrosion.	Install a casing to protect the chain. Periodically clean and lubricate the chains.

(1) Static fracture. The type of fracture found when subjecting the chain to the breakage test. Occurs when chain is subjected to a load greater than its breakage strength.

(2) Fatigue fracture. Occurs when the pin is repetitively subjected to loads greater than its fatigue limit. Recheck the size of the peak load and formulate a countermeasure.

(3) Shock-induced bending fracture. The pin is subjected to a large shock load. A pin is especially susceptible to this when the surface is corroded.

Figure 7.14 (iii) Pin

Symptom	Possible Causes	Remedy
Pin rotates or begins to stick out.	Excessive load or improper lubrication.	Replace with new chain. Improve the lubrication or loading conditions.
 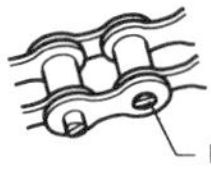 Normal	Operating a chain at high load without proper lubrication can create friction between the pin and bushing, causing the pin to rotate. In this condition, the pin may come out, leading to chain breakage.	Replace with new chain immediately. Do not weld or reuse the pins. (Dispose of the old chain to be sure that it is not used by mistake.) Also, if the pin head or link plate surface is worn, check the installation.
Wear or rust occurs only at the connecting pin in a tension application or similar operation.	Improper initial lubrication at installation.	Replace the connecting link. If pin wear is excessive, replace the chain also. Take special care to properly install the connecting section for devices such as terminators used for tension applications.

Figure 7.14 (iii) Pin (Cont.)

Symptom	Possible Causes	Remedy
Roller and/or bushing splits and falls off.	Excessive load or speed of rotation.	Choose a different chain according to the transmission capacity table.
	Inadequate lubrication.	Replace the chain. Provide adequate lubrication according to the operating conditions.
Fatigue fracture.  	Reached the point of fatigue during operation and eventually broke. Impact by the sprocket teeth at a force exceeding the chain's transmission capacity.	
Roller does not rotate.	RS11SS, RS15, RS25, RS35.	A bushed chain and not a roller chain is being used.
	The inner plate is moving inward, or the bushing is cracked.	Replace with a new chain. Re-inspect the installation and load conditions.
	Foreign particles have gotten between the bushing and roller.	Periodically clean the chain. Install a casing to protect the chain.
Roller is opening up.	Excessive load.  	Reduce the load. Provide adequate lubrication.
Roller is becoming hourglass shaped.	Excessive load or inadequate lubrication.	Replace with new chain. Improve the lubrication or loading conditions.

Figure 7.14 (iv) Bushing / Roller Problems

7.2 LARGE PITCH CONVEYOR CHAINS

7.2.1 Installation

Large pitch conveyor chain is usually supplied in the length specified. Therefore, you don't need to cut these chains. Disconnect the outer plate on the end of each chain set and use this as a connecting link.

Tools: hammer, setting tool, monkey wrench, or T-pin bender

Method (Figure 7.15)

Step 1. At the outer link on the end of the chain, the outer plate on the T-pin side is pushed in lightly. Remove the outer plate with the hammer.

Step 2. Using this outer link, connect the inner links of both ends of the chain.

Step 3. Tap the outer link plate onto the link with the hammer until the pin is completely inserted into the link plate.

Step 4. When you see the T-pin hole, insert the new T-pin into it. Using the monkey wrench or T-pin bender, bend the T-pin more than 30° to lock it into place.

Outside Link

Inside Link

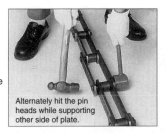

Alternately hit the pin heads while supporting other side of plate.

Figure 7.15   Installation of a Large Pitch Conveyor Chain

7.2.2 Installation Accuracy

After installing the chain, you need to check the accuracy of the installation. This involves verifying the amount of tension and the precise positioning of the shafts.

7.2.2.1 Chain Tension

Gently lift the chain at the driven end behind the driven sprocket (where the chain tension is minimum). You should be able to move the chain slightly. This provides adequate play when the chain is running.

If you are running more than one chain and they each have take-ups, adjust each take-up so that the chains are equal in tension (Figure 7.16).

7.2.2.2 Horizontal Precision and Parallelism of the Shafts

Refer to the method shown in Basics Section 7.1.2. The inclination between A and B should be within ± 1 mm.

7.2.2.3 Accuracy of the Rails

Check the rails. The connections should be smooth with no gaps. Figure 7.17 (i) shows examples of good connections; Figure 7.17 (ii) shows examples of bad connections.

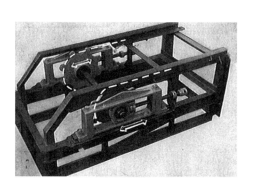

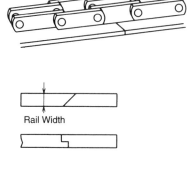

Rail Width

Figure 7.16 Adjust Take-Up so Chains Are Equal   **Figure 7.17 (i)** Examples of Good Rail Connections

7.2.3 Start-Up

After you install the chain, you must lubricate it. In addition, check the points in Basics Section 7.1.3. In addition to those shown, look at the following:

1. The rails and the sprockets are installed properly.
2. The rollers rotate smoothly.

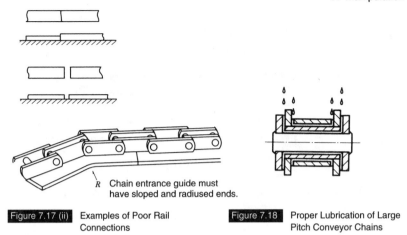

<table>
<tr><td>R</td><td>Chain entrance guide must have sloped and radiused ends.</td></tr>
</table>

R Chain entrance guide must have sloped and radiused ends.

| **Figure 7.17 (ii)** | Examples of Poor Rail Connections | **Figure 7.18** | Proper Lubrication of Large Pitch Conveyor Chains |

7.2.4 Lubrication

Proper lubrication is very important for chain operation. The manufacturer usually ships large pitch conveyor chain without lubrication or rust protection. Therefore, before start-up, you must apply lubricating oil, such as SAE30 or SAE40, by brush or drip. You should lubricate mainly the bushings and rollers (Figure 7.18).

To maximize the life of your chain during normal operation, lubricate it at least once a week.

> *NOTE: Lubricate more often immediately after you install the chain and if the chain is used in harsh conditions (for example, at high speed, high load, high temperature).*

7.2.5 Inspection

A chain is a very reliable part of a conveying machine. You can expect very long life from a chain if you've followed the selection and operating guidelines properly.

However, it is important to inspect a chain periodically to make sure it is operating correctly. During long-term use, pins, bushings, and rollers gradually wear. An unexpected shock load or the operating environment may cause problems. To avoid any accidents caused by these factors, you must regularly inspect the items shown in Figure 7.19, and address any problems as described in Basics Section 7.2.6. Plan at least monthly inspections. If the chain is used in harsh conditions, inspect it more frequently.

7.2.6 Troubleshooting and Problem-Solving

If you find something wrong with a chain during start-up or regular inspection, it may require treatment as shown in Figure 7.19, or you may need to change to a different type of chain.

Basics

Symptom	Possible Causes	Remedy
Excessive wear at the inside of the chain's link plates or the teeth surfaces. 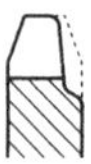	Improper centering of the sprocket.	Remove the chain and correct the centering of the drive and driven sprockets.
	The chain is being pushed to the side.	Remove the cause of the push and/or install a guide roller.
	Vibration caused by the inaccurate finishing of the sprocket's axle hole.	Check and correct the faulty locations and replace the sprocket with a new part.
Improper flex or bending of the chain.	Rusting or corrosion.	Install a partition to protect the chain. Select a chain of suitable specification (for example, MT type).
	Particles of the conveyed material have contaminated the pin, roller, and bushings. Otherwise, contamination from foreign particles.	Install a partition to protect the chain. Select a chain with large clearance between the pin, bushing, and roller.
	Deformation of the chain caused by improper installation.	Inspect and correct the installation of the sprockets and axles.
	Inadequate lubrication.	Inspect the lubrication or look into wear-resistant chain (for example, CT or BT specification).
	Operation in extremely high temperatures (over 400°C).	Provide adequate clearance.
	Seizure from excessive loads.	Provide periodic lubrication. Reduce load.
	Pin bending due to excessively high loading.	Reduce load.
The chain is winding on the sprocket.	Too much slack in the chain.	Adjust the chain length or distance between axles, or install a tensioner.
	Excessively worn sprocket. The chain and sprocket do not match.	Replace the chain and/or sprocket with the correct-sized part.
The chain is climbing up on the sprocket. 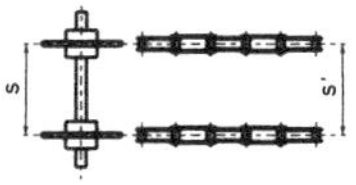	The chain and sprocket do not match.	Replace the chain or sprocket with the correct-sized part.
	The total arc of contact with the chain on the sprocket is insufficient.	Have the total arc of contact be at least three teeth on the sprocket.
	Excessive load.	Reduce the load (for example, by installing a shock absorber).
	Inadequate back-tension.	Adjust the catenary or take-up idler, or install a tensioner.
	Excessive elongation of the chain due to wear.	Replace with a new chain.
	The distance between the center of the chain and the sprocket do not match.	Inspect and correct.
Unusual noises.	Inadequate lubrication to the contacting portions of the pin and bushing.	Provide sufficient lubrication.
	Inadequate lubrication to the contacting portions of the bushing and roller.	Provide sufficient lubrication. Use a bearing roller or plastic roller.
	Winding or rising on the sprocket.	See previous symptom.
	Loose chain casing or axle bearing.	Tighten all nuts and bolts.
	Interference of the casing with the chain or other moving part.	Inspect and correct.
	Excessive wear in the chain or sprocket.	Replace the chain or sprocket. (Replace all chains connected.)
	Improper setting of the guide rail. 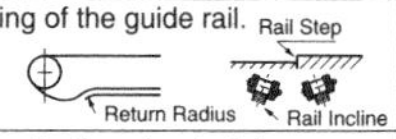	Inspect and correct.
Rusting of the chain.	Inappropriate selection of material.	Select a more suitable chain material. Protect the chain from the environment. Apply a rust inhibitor.
	Condensation.	Eliminate the temperature difference between inside and outside of conveyor (using insulation, etc.).
Improper roller spin and uneven roller wear.	Excessive load on roller.	Provide sufficient lubrication. Consider bearing roller or GT chain specification.
	Particles of the conveyed material, or other foreign particles, have gotten between bushing and roller.	Periodic cleaning. Install partition to protect chain.
	Particles of the conveyed material, or other foreign particles, have built up onto the rail.	Periodic cleaning. Install partition to protect chain.
	The lubricant is falling on the roller surface and rail without entering between the bushing and roller, and between the roller and link plate.	Select the appropriate lubricant and lubrication method.
	The bushing and roller have rusted together.	Select the appropriate specifications (RT, etc.).
	The inner plate is moving sideward.	Replace with a new chain. Re-inspect the installation and load conditions.
	The bushing is cracked.	Reduce the load and lower the speed of rotation.
	The side surface of the roller is contacting the side of the link plate due to a thrust load.	Eliminate the cause of the thrust load.
	The chain and sprocket do not match. Excessively worn teeth.	Check for tooth deformation.

Figure 7.19 (i)   Troubleshooting Large Pitch Conveyor Chain

Symptom	Possible Causes	Remedy
The roller is opening up.	Excessive load.	Reduce the load, provide adequate lubrication, remove any large steps in the rail.
The roller or bushing is split (falling off).	Excessive load.	Reduce the load. Provide adequate lubrication.
	The number of teeth is too few with respect to the conveyor speed.	Increase the number of teeth. Decrease the speed.
The roller is becoming hour-glass shaped.	Excessive load or inadequate lubrication.	Increase the lubrication, improve loading conditions, and replace the chain with a new one.
	Excessively worn rail.	Correct or replace the rail.
The chain sticks and slips. (This can be caused by a combination of many problems. Therefore, the listed remedies may not solve the problem.)	Change the rolling friction coefficient of the chain.	Lubricate the chain and clean the rail. Lubricate with Tsubaki oil. Change to a bearing roller chain.
	The conveyor speed is too slow.	Increase the speed.
	Insufficient rigidity in the frame. The conveyor chain is small compared to the device.	Increase the frame rigidity; increase the chain model number. Decrease the slack in the drive roller chain.
	The force of friction is excessively large.	Lubricate the chain. Change to a bearing roller chain.
	The machine is too long.	Divide the conveyor system into sections to decrease the length.
	Inconsistent speeds due to movement along a polygon-shaped path.	Use a 12- or-more-toothed drive sprocket.
Excessive wear of the sprocket teeth valleys and drive sides.	Excessively worn chain.	Replace both the chain and sprocket.
	Insufficient number of teeth.	Increase the number of teeth.
	A BF chain (no rollers) is being used.	Change to an RF chain (with rollers).
	The hardness of the teeth is insufficient with respect to the load and conveyed material or foreign particles.	Use a sprocket with hardened teeth or changeable teeth.
	The chain and sprocket do not match.	Replace the chain or sprocket with one that is of the correct size.
Excessive wear of the inside link and pin on one side of an NF block chain or BF chain (no roller).	Increased internal tension when meshing with the sprocket.	Attach the supporting block to the sprocket. Reduce the load. Lubricate the chain and sprocket. 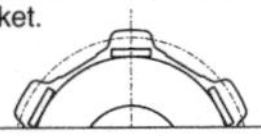
Sudden fracture of the link plate.	Excessive load.	Eliminate causes of the overloading. Install a safety device (for example, Shock Relay). Increase chain size.
	Weakening of chain caused by excessive wear or corrosion.	Replace with new part. Install a cover to protect the chain. Periodically lubricate chain. Select a chain with the proper specifications for the application.
	The link plates are pressed outward by the sprocket. 	Check and correct the installation. Excessively worn chain or sprocket. Check if the chain and sprocket match, and correct as necessary.
Crack in the link plate. (1) Fatigue breakage. 	Excessive load or excessively large repetitive load.	Eliminate overloading or large repetitive loads.
	The factor of safety is not sufficient.	Increase the size or specifications of the chain to increase the factor of safety. Replace with a new chain.
	Repetitive load on attachment.	Eliminate overloading or large repetitive loads; increase the chain size to increase the allowable load of the attachment.

Figure 7.19 (ii) Troubleshooting Large Pitch Conveyor Chain

Symptom	Possible Causes	Remedy
(2) Corrosion stress crack. (Bow-shaped crack in heat-treated metal plates.) 	The chain is being used in an acidic or alkaline environment. (This is not caused by a repetitive load.)	Install a cover to protect the chain from the environment. Replace with new part. Use a chain with a high resistance to corrosion stress cracks.
Deformed link plate holes and pin rotation (the pin is shifted from its normal position). 	Excessive load.	Eliminate the cause of overloading and replace chain with a larger size.
	Improper installation of the connecting link.	Replace connecting link with a new one.
	Excessive load and inadequate lubrication.	Replace with a new chain and improve the lubrication and loading conditions.
	Seizure of the pin and bushing, improper bending or flex of the chain.	Increase the chain size. Increase the clearance between the pin and bushing.
(1) Pin fatigue fracture. (2) Pin corrosive fatigue. (3) Pin brittle fracture. (4) Pin sudden fracture. 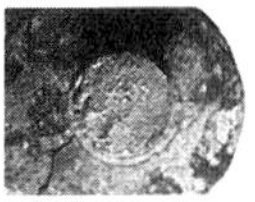	The factor of safety used for calculation of the peak load versus the breakage load was too small. The peak load acted like a repetitive load on the chain.	Recheck the size of the peak load, and eliminate its cause. Replace the chain with a larger size (larger pin diameter).
	The pin was subjected to a tensile load at the side of the fracture origin, where the break then progressed. Chain is especially susceptible to this when the pin surface is corroded and weak against bending stresses.	Recheck the size of the peak load, and eliminate its cause. Replace the chain with a larger size (larger pin diameter). Use a pin made of an anti-corrosive material.
	Poor environment.	Use an appropriate pin material.
	Excessive load.	Eliminate the cause of overloading, and replace chain with a larger size.
Excessive wear caused by the conveyed material. The surface is worn away. 	The chain is contaminated with especially abrasive materials, such as mineral powders, etc., being worn away by the chain surface itself.	Prevent material from falling onto the chain. Use a wear-resistant chain.
Excessive wear from corrosion. Link plates not made from an anti-corrosive material are corroding. 	The chain is exposed to acidic or alkaline substances, and, therefore, more susceptible to machine wear, which then progresses much faster.	Use a material not affected by the chemicals. Use a wear-resistant material for the machine-worn parts.
Excessive wear from electro-chemical corrosion. Only the contact surfaces are worn. 	When the chain is covered with water or passes through a solvent, the portions in contact suffer galvanic corrosion.	Use a material not affected by the chemicals. Use a wear-resistant material for the machine-worn parts.

Figure 7.19 (iii) Troubleshooting Large Pitch Conveyor Chain

1. TRANSMISSION CHAINS

Power transmission chains are classified into six major groups.

1.1 Standard Roller Chains. These chains are designed for general usage.

1.2 High Performance Chains. These chains have higher tensile strength and greater fatigue strength.

1.3 Lube-Free Chains. These chains have longer wear life than standard chains without lubrication.

1.4 Environmentally Resistant Chains. Chains with special corrosion resistance.

1.5 Specialty Chains, Type 1. For specific applications.

1.6 Specialty Chains, Type 2. For general designs.
  Within these six groups, there are many types of chains available (Figure 1.1). In the following sections, we will discuss the various types.

Figure 1.1   Power Transmission Chains

1.1 STANDARD ROLLER CHAINS

1.1.1 ANSI Roller Chains (RS)

Transmission: General usage

Application Example

Power transmission chains are widely used throughout the world in a variety of applications, including drive, tension, shuttle traction, and transmission reduction operations. Because of this widespread usage, certain international standards are set to ensure that pitch, width, and other key characteristics of chains and sprockets are standardized. In the United States, power transmission chains must meet ANSI B29.1, thus earning the name ANSI chains. In other countries, the chains must meet JIS B1801, ISO 606A, or ISO 1395C.

Construction and Features

(1) ANSI Roller Chains have the same shape and construction as the chain shown in Basics Section 1.1.1. There are 14 sizes of roller chains regulated by ANSI. For easy reference, these are numbered 25, 35, 41, 40, 50, 60, 80, 100, 120, 140, 160, 180, 200, and 240. Some manufacturers include chain numbers 320 and 400 to the list of standardized chains.

(2) Chains with a "5" on the right-hand digit of the chain number are bushing chains. Bushing chains do not have rollers.

(3) Number 41 chain is a narrow variation of number 40.

(4) This chain number indicates the chain pitch. Here's how to decipher the pitch from the chain number. The numbers to the left of the right-hand digit refer to the chain pitch in eighths of an inch. To calculate the pitch, multiply the number by 3.175 mm. For example: 140 = 14 × 3.175 = 44.45 mm pitch, or 14/8 = 1.75 inches.

(5) Each manufacturer adds its own identification stamp prior to the chain number. For Tsubaki, "RS" is the identifier (for example, RS80, RS100). The use of "RS" as an identifier has spread widely; it has become the standard symbol for power transmission roller chains.

(6) There are smaller chains available. Refer to the "Miniature Chain" Section in this book for information on sizes smaller than number 25.

Sprockets

Various sprockets are produced for each size of RS Roller Chain. Sprockets are identified by the type of base material used in manufacture and by the bore. Here are some basic types:

(1) Carbon steel sprockets with plain bores. (Sintered metal or cast iron are sometimes used.)
(2) Carbon steel sprockets with finished bores, keyway, and setscrews. TAPER-LOCK® and QD® bores are also available.
(3) 304 stainless steel sprockets with plain bores.
(4) Engineered plastic sprockets with plain bores.
(5) POWER-LOCK® sprockets, which do not require a keyway or setscrew.

Selection and Handling
See Chapters 4 through 7 in the Basics Section.

1.1.2 BS/DIN Roller Chain

Transmission: General usage

Application Example
BS/DIN power transmission chains are regulated by international standards (ISO 606B) and are used primarily in Europe. In Japan and the United States, BS/DIN chains are used in transmission equipment imported from European countries or for licensed production.

Selection and Handling
Compared to the same-sized ANSI Roller Chains, the power ratings of BS/DIN chains in drive applications (tent curve) are a little lower (Table 1.1).

Table 1.1 Power Ratings for Standard ANSI and BS/DIN Roller Chains

Chain No.	Pitch (mm)	Number of Sprocket Teeth	RPM (rev./min.)	Power Rating (kW)
RS80	25.4	19	500	24.1
RS16B	25.4	19	500	22.0
RS160	50.8	19	500	76.1
RS32B	50.8	19	500	70.0

TAPER-LOCK ® is a registered trademark of Reliance Electric Company. QD® is a registered trademark of and is used under license from Emerson Electric Company.

1.2 HIGH PERFORMANCE CHAINS

These are enhanced types of ANSI Roller Chain (RS) in average tensile strength and/or fatigue resistance. Each chain has different features. Figure 1.2 shows the general relationship of high performance chains to ANSI Standard Roller Chain.

NOTE: The multipliers shown in Figure 1.2 compare high performance chain to RS Roller Chain. The comparisons are between products of Tsubaki. You may find the ratio varies by chain size or manufacturer. Refer to a specific manufacturer's catalog for details.

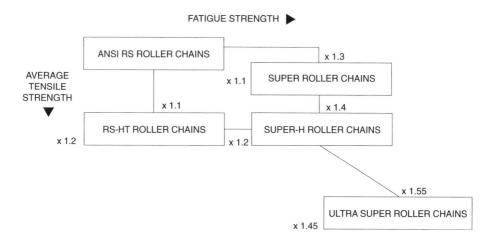

Figure 1.2   Increasing Fatigue Strength and Tensile Strength of Roller Chains

1.2.1 Super Roller Chain

High performance: General uses

Application Example

Super Roller Chains are generally used in compact drives because they have high maximum allowable tension. (See Figure 1.3.)

Figure 1.3 Super Roller Chain

Construction and Features

Super Roller Chains are constructed for added fatigue strength (Table 1.2). In addition, there are several characteristics that distinguish Super Roller Chains.

(1) Appearance
- The plate shape is almost flat.
- Quad-staked riveting on the pin helps hold the link plate.
- The roller is seamless, not curled.

(2) Construction
- The pins are made of through hardened steel, which provides toughness rather than surface hardness.
- The link plate holes are ball drifted. This process involves pressing a steel ball through the hole of the link plate. The steel ball is slightly larger than the diameter of the hole, which creates residual compressive stress.

Table 1.2 Super Roller Chain Compared to ANSI Standard Roller Chain

	Average Tensile Strength	Maximum Allowable Load
RS100	118 kN	22.6 kN
SUPER 100	127 kN	30.4 kN
Ratio	1.08	1.35

- Connecting link plates are press fit to maintain the higher fatigue resistance.
- The middle link plates of multiple strand chain's connecting link are not press fit. They are specially constructed for higher fatigue strength.
- Connecting links are fitted with high-strength spring pins.

Because of these features, Super Roller Chains offer higher maximum allowable tension, greater tensile strength, and increased shock resistance. Table 1.2 shows a comparison between Number 100 Super Roller Chain and Standard Roller Chain. Number 100 Super Roller Chain performs at the same level as RS120. Both have a maximum allowable tension of 30.4 kN.

Sprockets

High performance chain usually requires carbon steel sprockets. Cast iron sprockets with few teeth may lack adequate strength. Steel sprockets are available for single or multiple strand. Check the keyway strength of the sprockets before ordering to make sure they provide enough strength.

Selection and Handling

Super Roller Chains are available in sizes 80 through 240. Smaller chains ($\leq$60), stainless steel chains, and offset links are not available in Super Roller Chain.

When installing Super Roller Chain, do not use the connecting link from Standard Roller Chain. Only special press fit connecting links should be used with Super Roller Chains.

Super Roller Chains are susceptible to wear and elongation. Therefore, it is very important to provide proper lubrication. (Refer to manufacturer's catalog for details.)

1.2.2 Super-H Roller Chain

Heavy transmission

Application Example

Super-H Roller Chains are used in compact and heavy drives. (See Figure 1.4.) They have greater maximum allowable load, increased tensile strength, and smaller elastic elongation compared to the same-sized RS Roller Chain.

Figure 1.4   Super-H Roller Chain

Construction and Features

The link plates on Super-H Roller Chain are thicker. In fact, the thickness of the link plate is the same as the next-larger-sized Super Roller Chains. Table 1.3 compares data on number 100 chains.

Table 1.3 Super-H Roller Chain Compared to ANSI Standard Roller Chain

	Average Tensile Strength	Maximum Allowable Load
RS100	118 kN	22.6 kN
SUPER 100-H	145 kN	32.4 kN
Ratio	1.23	1.43

1.2.3 RS-HT Roller Chain

Heavy transmission: Construction machines, agriculture machines, and tension applications

Application Example

RS-HT Roller Chains have higher tensile strength and less elastic elongation in comparison with RS Roller Chains. These characteristics are good for "lifting" applications (at low cycles), construction machines, and agriculture equipment (Figure 1.5).

Figure 1.5 RS-HT Roller Chain

Construction and Features

Compared with RS Roller Chains, RS-HT Roller Chains have the features shown below and in Table 1.4.

Appearance

(1) Link plate thickness is equal to the next-larger chain.
(2) Quad-staked riveting on the pin head helps hold the link plate on the pin.
(3) Rollers are seamless, not curled.

Table 1.4 RS-HT Roller Chain Compared to ANSI Standard Roller Chain

	Average Tensile Strength	Maximum Allowable Load
RS100	118 kN	22.6 kN
RS100-HT	142 kN	24.5 kN
Ratio	1.20	1.08

1.2.4 Ultra Super Chain

Super-heavy transmission

Application Example
Ultra Super Chain has the highest tensile strength and greatest allowable tension of any chain that can mate with a standard sprocket. These features also allow the drive train of the equipment to be smaller. (See Figure 1.6.)

Figure 1.6   Ultra Super Roller Chain

Construction and Features
Ultra Super Chains have the same chain pitch, roller diameter, and width between inner link plates as ANSI Standard Chain. However, the link plate thickness is the same as the next-larger chain. The pin diameter is larger than ANSI Standard Chains. Table 1.5 compares RS100 Roller Chain and 100 Ultra Super Chain. In this chain series, both the average tensile strength and maximum allowable tension are increased, even over Super-H Chains. Number 100 Ultra Super Chains have the same maximum tension as RS140, which is two sizes larger.

Table 1.5 Comparison of ANSI Standard Chain (RS) with Ultra Super Chain (US)

	Average Tensile Strength	Maximum Allowable Load
RS100	118 kN	22.6 kN
US100	172 kN	39.2 kN
Ratio	1.45	1.73

Sprockets
See "Super Roller Chain" Section.

Selection and Handling
(1) Choose these chains using the guidelines for low-speed selection.
(2) Ultra Super Chain is available in sizes 100 through 240.
    (Number 180 is not available.)

(3) Ultra Super Chain is not available in multiple strand.

(4) Due to the hardness of plates being higher than other carbon steel roller chains, Ultra Super Chains have a greater risk of hydrogen embrittlement. Other points of notice are the same as Super-H Roller Chain.

1.3 LUBE-FREE CHAINS

1.3.1 LAMBDA® Roller Chain

Transmission and conveyor: Lube-free type, drive transmission

Application Example

LAMBDA Roller Chains do not require additional lubrication. This makes them ideal for "clean" applications like final assembly areas, paper production, and other operations where lubrication could affect the product on line. LAMBDA Roller Chains are available in drive or conveyor styles. (See Figure 1.7.)

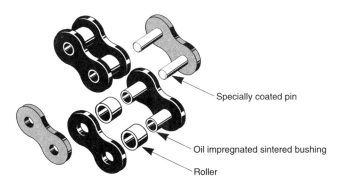

Specially coated pin

Oil impregnated sintered bushing

Roller

Figure 1.7   LAMBDA® Lube-Free Chain

Construction and Features

LAMBDA Roller Chains are designed for long wear life without additional lubrication. The bushings are made of oil-impregnated sintered metal, and the pins are specially coated. LAMBDA Roller Chains also have rollers, which make them different from other lube-free chains. (The SL series, for example, does not have rollers.)

The features of LAMBDA Roller Chains are as follows:

(1) LAMBDA Roller Chains outlast Standard Roller Chains without lubrication up to 30 times longer at low speed (about 25 m/min.) and seven times longer at medium speed (about 127 m/min.). (See Figure 1.8.)

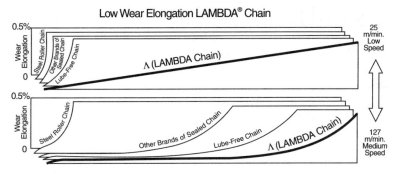

Low Wear Elongation LAMBDA® Chain

Figure 1.8   Comparison of LAMBDA® Chains and Other Chains

(2) The rollers on LAMBDA® Roller Chain engage the sprocket more smoothly, reducing power loss.

(3) LAMBDA Roller Chains have the same transmission capacity as equivalently sized ANSI Roller Chains at speeds of 150 m/min. or less.

(4) Because additional lubrication is not required, LAMBDA Roller Chains help prevent contamination of equipment and conveyed objects. This promotes a clean working environment.

(5) LAMBDA Roller Chains are designed to operate in temperatures from -10° to 60°C.

Sprockets

Single strands of LAMBDA Roller Chain run on standard sprockets. Multiple strand chains require special sprockets that have a wider transverse pitch.

Selection and Handling

(1) Drive LAMBDA Roller Chains have thicker roller link plates than RS Roller Chains. The chains are also wider. Check to make sure that the wider chains will run correctly on your equipment.

(2) When the chain is used in a dusty environment, the dust will absorb the lubrication oil in the bushings, and the bushings may wear in a short time. If conditions are dusty, test the chain in the environment.

(3) If LAMBDA Roller Chain is used in water, the chain will wear faster.

(4) When the lubricating oil contained in the bushing is depleted, the chain should be replaced.

Application Series

(1) Nickel-plated LAMBDA Roller Chain is available for higher corrosion resistance.

(2) LAMBDA II lasts twice as long as LAMBDA in temperatures up to 150°C.

1.3.2 Sealed Roller Chain

Lube-free type: High-speed transmission, in dusty conditions

Application Example

Sealed Roller Chain may be useful for general industrial applications that run at high speeds or in dusty conditions. (See Figure 1.9.)

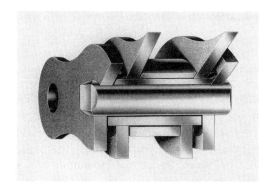

Figure 1.9   Sealed Roller Chain

Construction and Features

Sealed Roller Chains have O-ring seals between the pin link and the roller link plates. These seals keep the lubricant in and contaminants out. The inner width of the chain is the same as ANSI specifications. The total width of the chain is larger than the ANSI measurement because the bushings usually extend beyond the roller link plates to protect the O-rings.

Sealed Roller Chains are available in sizes 40 through 100. The average tensile strength is slightly lower than ANSI Roller Chain.

Sprockets

Standard sprockets are used for single strand chain.

Selection and Handling

(1) O-ring seals are usually made of acrylonitrile-butadiene rubber, which is highly resistant to oil, heat, and abrasion. Fluorine rubber O-ring seals are available for high heat operations (greater than 120°C).

(2) The link plates holding the O-rings are under compression. This means greater force is required to articulate the chain, and the transmitted power is decreased. At places where the chain tension is low (such as the return side) the strand will retain the bend. The manufacturing tolerances of the O-rings are generally large, therefore, it is difficult to make the bending resistance of O-ring chain smaller and stable.

(3) When the oil film between the O-ring and the link plate is gone, the O-ring will wear and deteriorate. Rubber has a "creeping" property, and it tries to make the contacting surface flat. Therefore, it becomes more difficult to get the lubricant into the working parts.

(4) During long-term operation, the O-rings may start to fall off the chain. Then, the elongation at that spot will progress very rapidly. If this occurs, it is time to replace the chain, even if the total chain has not reached the elongation limit (1.5 percent).

(5) The cost of Sealed Roller Chain is higher than ANSI Standard Roller Chain. The higher cost is because of the additional and special parts (O-ring seals, longer pins and bushings). Unfortunately, less expensive standard components cannot be used for Sealed Roller Chain.

Technical Trend

Chain manufacturers are constantly striving to improve the quality and wear life of chains in general, including Sealed Roller Chain.

In the area of seal research, a variety of shapes of seals has been tested. The goal is to reduce the bending resistance and yet keep the lubricant in the working parts. Currently, O-rings are the most practical alternative.

1.4 ENVIRONMENTALLY RESISTANT CHAINS

These are chains that offer high resistance to corrosion or heat due to special coatings or materials. The approximate relationship between these chains is shown in Figure 1.10.

Table 1.6 shows a variety of environmentally resistant chains and materials.

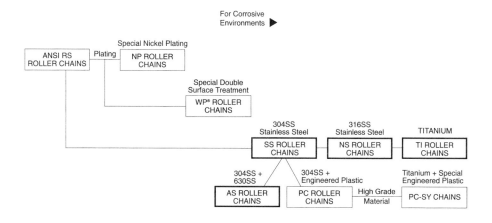

NOTE: The chains surrounded with a thick line have a temperature range of -20° to 400°C. Before using these chains in temperatures outside this range, contact the manufacturer.

In this Figure, the left-to-right direction shows the relative corrosion resistance (right is more resistant than left). The average tensile strength or maximum allowable tension may differ even between chains of the same size.

Figure 1.10   Environmentally Resistant Chains

Table 1.6 Chains for Special Environments

Series	Treatment	Special Features and Applications	Conditions						
			Water	Sea Water	Sanitary	Chemicals, Acid, Alkalis, Corrosives	Low/High Temperatures	Non-Magnetic	Lube-Free
NP	Nickel-plated	1. Maximum allowable load about 10% less than RS Chain. 2. Use SS in applications that contact food.	•						
WP®	Special coating	1. Maximum allowable load same as RS Chain. 2. Better than NP in wet applications. 3. Use SS in applications that contact food.	•	•					
SS	304SS	1. Typical anti-corrosion chain. 2. Food, chemical, and pharmaceutical environments.	•	•	•	•	•		
NS	316SS	1. Very corrosion resistant. 2. Maximum allowable load same as SS Chain.	•	•	•	•	•	•	
AS	Precipitation-hardened stainless + 304SS	1. Maximum allowable load 50% higher than SS Chain. 2. A little less anti-corrosive than SS.	•	•	•	•	•		
PC	304SS + engineered plastic bushing link (white)	1. Low noise (5 dB less than steel chain). 2. Light weight (50% less than steel chain).	•	•	•	•			•
PC-SY	Titanium + special engineered plastic bushing link (glossless)	1. Resists chemicals, including hydrochloric and sulfuric acids. 2. Suitable when stainless steel cannot be used.			•	•		•	•
TI	Titanium	1. Nonmagnetic and high resistance to corrosion. 2. Light weight (50% less than steel chain).	•	•	•	•	•	•	

1.4.1 Nickel-Plated Roller Chain (NP)

Transmission, conveyor: Mild corrosive environment

Application Example

Nickel-Plated Roller Chains combine strength close to ANSI Roller Chain with the corrosion resistance that comes from the nickel plating. These chains are used in applications where you want light corrosion resistance. For example, NP chain might be used in an application that has limited contact with water. (See Figure 1.11.)

Construction and Features

Plated Roller Chains have corrosion resistance and the attractive appearance of nickel plating for a low cost. The strength and wear resistance are almost the same as standard chains. These chains are a good buy if they are selected correctly. Numbers 25 through 120 are standard.

Generally, small pitch chains are plated before assembling, and large pitch chains are plated after assembling. Either way, the interior surfaces of the components may not receive complete coverage.

Sprockets

Standard sprockets are used. When the application requires no rust, use stainless steel or engineered plastic sprockets. With engineered plastic sprockets, the strength and speed (less than 70 m/min.) are limited.

Selection and Handling

(1) Plated Roller Chains, however well plated, will experience flaking of the plating from the interior surfaces and the roller surface that rotates on the roller guide and impacts the sprocket. If this flaking presents a problem (for example, danger of flakes getting mixed into foods), use stainless steel chains.

(2) Nickel has a higher electrical potential than the base metal. If the nickel plating flakes off, corrosion will progress faster at that point. Zinc plating has a lower electrical potential than the base metal, therefore, the corrosion will progress more slowly. But frequent exposure to acid during the zinc-plating process increases the likelihood of hydrogen embrittlement in the hardened plates. Therefore, zinc plating is not available for some chains.

(3) Nickel plating may also create hydrogen embrittlement. In an application where a broken chain may create serious damage, WP® series chain may be a better choice. Of course, safety guards must be installed.

(4) Link plates are shot peened for greater fatigue strength. The plating process reduces the effects of shot peening, therefore, the fatigue strength of plated chain is 10 percent less than that of standard chains.

(5) Plated Roller Chains are prelubricated with mineral oil after assembly. If the prelubrication is unwanted, advise the manufacturer when ordering.

Figure 1.11   Nickel-Plated Chain

1.4.2 WP® Roller Chain

Transmission: Corrosion-resistant type

Application Example

WP Roller Chains offer the strength and durability of ANSI Roller Chains plus a special surface treatment that stands up to water, and even sea water.

Construction and Features

WP Roller Chains are mechanically coated to resist rust. Mechanical coating is different than applying electroplating, or chemically plating the components. Some manufacturers produce chemically plated chains. To chemically plate chains, zinc and chrome are used in a high-temperature process. The chains resist rusting when the chlorine ion is present. However, if the chains are chemically plated after assembly, press-fit parts will lose some of the interference due to exposure to high temperatures. This decreases the maximum allowable tension. Also the hardness of the working parts is decreased, which reduces the wear resistance.

In WP Roller Chains, zinc and chrome are used, and the rust resistance to chlorine ions is the same as that of chemically plated chains. But, because WP Roller Chains are not exposed to high temperatures during the mechanical plating process, they have higher maximum allowable tension. The surface of WP Roller Chain is olive-gray.

Selection and Handling

(1) The tensile strength and maximum allowable tension of WP Roller Chains are the same as those of Standard Roller Chains.

(2) Working temperature range is -10° to 60°C.

(3) Avoid using these chains if they will have direct contact with foods. The foods may become contaminated.

1.4.3 Stainless Steel Roller Chain (SS)

Transmission: Corrosive environment. Manufacture of foods, chemicals, and medicines

Application Example

All parts are made of austenitic 304 stainless steel.
The material composition is:
Carbon (C): less than 0.08%
Chromium (Cr): 18.00 to 20.00%
Nickel (Ni): 8.00 to 10.50%

SS Roller Chains are the most commonly used environmentally resistant chains for the manufacture of foods, chemicals, medicines, or transmission in water. They are also used in indoor conditions where rust is a problem. (See Figure 1.12.)

Figure 1.12 Stainless Steel Chain

Construction and Features

The construction and sizes of SS Roller Chains are the same as ANSI Roller Chains. Each part is formed from 304 stainless steel by cold working processes, such as press processing and machining. The pins are assembled to the outer plates and the bushings to the inner plates. Neither solution annealing nor passivating treatment are done on SS Roller Chains.

SS Roller Chains have the following features:
- Attractive appearance of glossy stainless steel.
- Exceptional corrosion resistance. But in certain highly corrosive conditions, stress-corrosion cracking may occur.

- Exceptional corrosion resistance and strength at high temperatures. These chains can operate in high temperatures, but the manufacturer should be contacted for applications above 400°C.
- These chains may be used in extremely low temperatures, because low temperature brittleness does not occur.
- There is slight magnetism, due to the cold working processes.
- Due to the cold working processes, the surface of the chains may rust in some conditions.
- The tensile strength of SS chain is almost half that of RS Roller Chains.
- The chain parts are not heat-treated (such as quenching and tempering). The tensile strength and hardness of these parts are lower than that of RS Roller Chains.
- Because the surface hardness of the working parts (pins, bushings and rollers) is low, the wear resistance is also less than that of RS Roller Chains. Due to the lower thermal conductivity of stainless steel, the working parts retain more heat, which also lowers the allowable tension of SS Roller Chains. The allowable tension of the chain is determined by the wear resistance.
- Numbers 11 through 240 are available. (Number 15 is not available.) Only sizes smaller than number 80 are usually stocked. Nonhardened materials with low thermal conductivity must be designed with smaller press fits. This fact also makes the allowable tension of these chains lower than RS Roller Chains.

Sprockets

SS Roller Chains run on standard-sized sprockets. In corrosive conditions, stainless steel or engineered plastic (less than 70 m/min.) sprockets should be used. Carbon steel sprockets may corrode and contaminate the chain and the environment.

Selection and Handling

If SS Roller Chain is used in water within the allowable load published by the manufacturer, the water acts as a lubricant, and the chain has additional wear resistance. (See Figure 1.13.)

Check the manufacturer's catalog for the conditions when SS Roller Chain is appropriate.

When determining the allowable tension, do not consider the safety factor and/or the tensile strength of SS Roller Chains shown in manufacturers' catalogs. The tensile strength of SS Roller Chain has no practical meaning.

Surface treatment of the working parts, such as platings or nitriding, may improve the wear resistance of SS Roller Chains, but the coating may peel off and contaminate the environment. Nitriding usually reduces the corrosion resistance of the chains. Contact the manufacturer for additional information.

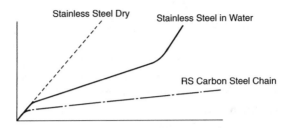

Stainless Steel Dry

Stainless Steel in Water

RS Carbon Steel Chain

Figure 1.13   Use of Stainless and Standard Chain in Water

When chains are cycled between the freezer and room temperature, dew forms and freezes on the chains. This may cause noise, difficult articulation, and chain breakage. Silicon grease applied to the gaps of the chain helps to prevent this.

When SS Roller Chains are used at temperatures greater than 400°C, extra clearance in the chain joints is required. The thermal expansion may cause the joints to seize and the chain to break. Advise the manufacturer of the operating temperature(s) in which the chain will be used.

You can extend the working life of SS Roller Chains with proper lubrication. The chains should be lubricated as much as possible when the application allows it.

Application Series

Other corrosion-resistant stainless steel chains are shown below. For conditions and size availability, check the manufacturer's catalog.

NS Series

All parts are made of austenitic stainless steel SS316.
The composition of this material is:

Carbon (C): less than 0.08%

Chromium (Cr): 16.00 to 18.00%

Nickel (Ni): 10.00 to 14.00%

Molybdenum (Mo): 2.00 to 3.00%

NS series chains cost more than SS Roller Chains but have greater resistance to corrosion and heat. When the chains are used in temperatures above 400°C, contact the manufacturer. The allowable tension is the same as SS Roller Chains. These chains are considered almost nonmagnetic.

AS Series

Pins, bushings, and rollers (double pitch oversized rollers are SS304) are made of precipitation-hardened stainless steel. The plates are made of the same material as SS Roller Chains. Due to the hardened pins and bushings, this series has higher wear resistance. The maximum allowable tension is 1.5 times that of SS Roller Chains. That means you can use a smaller chain and get equivalent performance. The corrosion resistance is less than SS Roller Chains. These chains are somewhat magnetic.

Other Precipitation-Hardened Series

There are other types of stainless steel chains that have case-hardened or all precipitation-hardened stainless steel components, including the link plates. The tensile strength is higher than SS Roller Chains, however, the wear resistance and the maximum allowable tension are the same. Talk with the manufacturer about the availability and applications of these chains.

SS Engineered Plastic Sleeve Series

The engineered plastic sleeve between the pins and bushings make this a lube-free variation of SS Roller Chains. These chains cannot typically work in water or other liquids with some exception, such as Tsubaki LS series, but are good for indoor conditions where rust should be avoided. The allowable tension is the same as SS Roller Chains.

TI Series

All parts are made of titanium or titanium alloy. These chains have greater corrosion resistance in chloric conditions and no magnetism. The chain's weight is very light (about half of the same-sized steel chain). The allowable tension is the same as SS Roller Chains.

Technical Trends

In stainless steel chain design, corrosion resistance is the most important factor. The allowable tension is much lower than RS Roller Chains. For example, the maximum allowable tension for RS80SS is 1.77 kN versus 14.7 kN for RS80. The allowable tension for SS Roller Chain is about one-eighth that of RS Roller Chain. In the AS series, the ratio is 1 to 5.5. Researchers continue to study ways of increasing wear resistance and allowable press fit at assembly.

1.4.4 Poly-Steel Chain (PC)

Transmission, conveyance: Lube-free type. Food or medicine production

Application Example

Poly-Steel (PC) Chains are lube-free chains used in food or medicine production. PC Chains can be used in power-transmission applications, and, with the addition of attachments on the outer plates, as conveyors. (See Figure 1.14.)

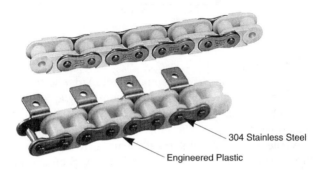

304 Stainless Steel
Engineered Plastic

Poly-Steel Chain

Construction and Features

The chains are a construction of outer links (outer plates and pins) made of SS304, and inner links made of engineered plastic. There are no rollers. Features are shown below.

(1) Inner links are made of a self-lubricating material; therefore, the chains do not require lubrication. The wear resistance of these chains is higher than that of Stainless Steel Roller Chains without lubrication (Figure 1.15).

(2) Because the inner link is made of plastic, the noise caused by engagement with the sprocket is lower (about 5 dB lower than Standard Roller Chain).

(3) PC Chain is very light; about half that of Standard Roller Chains.

(4) There are five sizes for this series: Numbers 25, 35, 40, 50, and 60. The maximum allowable tension varies from 0.08 to 0.88 kN.

Sprockets

Standard sprockets are used. The three major sizes have the same dimensions as ANSI Roller Chain; Numbers 25 and 35 are slightly wider. In corrosive conditions, carbon steel sprockets may corrode and contaminate the application. Use stainless steel or, at slow speeds (less than 70 m/min.), use engineered plastic sprockets.

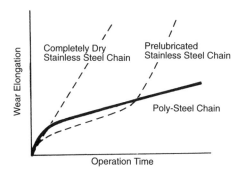

Figure 1.15 Stainless Steel Chain Versus Poly-Steel Chain

Selection and Handling

(1) One of the advantages of Stainless Steel Drive Chain is its high ratio between tensile strength and maximum allowable tension. Even if tension is high at the moment of starting, it will not break if the start-up is infrequent. The ratio between tensile strength and maximum allowable tension for Poly-Steel Chain, however, is low. There is a huge difference in the Young's ratio between steel and plastic. Almost all of the shock load is absorbed by the engineered plastic inner link. This means you need to take care when selecting Poly-Steel Chain. If Poly-Steel Chain is selected the same way as standard chain, breakage may occur. When selecting Poly-Steel Chain, the maximum tension—including inertia shock—must be considered to get satisfactory results.

(2) These chains are suitable for splash applications, but they should not be submerged in water or other liquids. The ideal environment is indoors where rusting must be avoided.

(3) The allowable tension of this series is almost the same as Stainless Steel Roller Chains (SS series.)

(4) An offset link is not available for Poly-Steel Chain. An even number of links must be used.

Application Series: PC-SY

Because of the titanium outer links and special engineered plastic inner links, SY series chains do not corrode in most chemicals, including hydrochloric and sulfuric acid. The allowable tension is about half that of Poly-Steel Chains. This is a nonmagnetic type of chain.

Technical Trend

Manufacturers are working to increase both the tensile strength and the maximum allowable tension.

1.5 SPECIALTY CHAINS, TYPE 1

1.5.1 Bicycle Chain

Transmission

Application Example

These chains transmit the power of pedaling to the back wheel (Figure 1.16). Most bikes use chain; a few styles use cog belts, but these are the exceptions. In the early stages of chain development, chain design grew in response to development in bicycles. Bicycles are categorized as shown in Table 1.7.

In addition to bicycles, these chains may be used in low-speed, light-load transmission operations, for example, in agriculture machines or with electric garage door openers.

Figure 1.16   Most Bicycles Use Chain

Table 1.7 Categories of Bicycles

Category	Models of Bicycles
General	Sports, small-tire, general-purpose, child's
Infant	Infant's
Special Purpose	Road racing, heavy-duty carriage, track racing, mountain, tricycle, tandem

Construction and Features

Bicycle Chains are generally categorized into two types: 1/2 × 1/8 and 1/2 × 3/32. The first number (1/2) is the chain pitch; the latter numbers (1/8 and 3/32, respectively) indicate the inner width in inches.

Number 1/2 × 1/8 chain is used for simple transmission without speed shifting; it has the same construction as Standard Roller Chain.

Number 1/2 × 3/32 chain is used with a derailleur. There are two types of construction—standard roller and bushingless (Table 1.8). In the bushingless chain, the inner link plates are extruded so that the inner plates also serve as the bushings (Figures 1.17 and 1.18). In most derailleur transmission chains, the link plates are bent or cut so that the chains can change smoothly on the front or rear sprockets.

Table 1.8 Applications of Bicycle Chains

Nominal Number	Pitch	Inner Link Width	Construction	Application
1/2 X 1/8	12.7	3.30	Roller Chain	Simple drive General purpose
1/2 X 3/32	12.7	2.38	Roller Chain Bushingless Chain	With derailleur Sports Racing

Figure 1.17 Bushingless Bicycle Chain Components

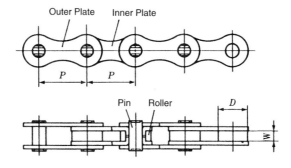

Figure 1.18 Schematic Diagram of Bushingless Bicycle Chain

Sprockets

The basic sizes of the sprockets (front and rear) are common to all manufacturers; however, the tooth shape is different. This is especially true for the sprockets for $1/2 \times 3/32$ chains. Each manufacturer designs its own tooth shapes for better shifting. Exercise care when changing sprockets.

Selection and Handling

(1) Manufacturers usually offer a selection system for derailleur transmission, which includes the chain and sprockets. Check the manufacturer's catalog for information.

(2) The chain's performance is usually influenced by wear. Select a chain with specially coated pins, which increase wear resistance.

(3) You must connect the chains carefully, or they may break during operation. Use special connecting pins (sold separately) to connect chains, especially those used with derailleurs.

(4) These chains are frequently exposed to rain, dirt, or mud, which can lead to elongation or rust. The chains need regular cleaning and lubrication.

(5) Do not use weak-acid rust remover (such as phosphatic rust remover) on these chains. These chemicals can cause hydrogen embrittlement and chain breakage.

Technical Trend

To keep up with the design enhancements of bicycles, chains are being developed in several ways:

(1) Lighter weight.
(2) Higher rust and weather resistance.
(3) Attractive appearance.
(4) Nonstaining to clothes.
(5) Lower noise at engagement.

1.5.2 Motorcycle Chain

Transmission

Application Examples

Motorcycles are high-speed applications that operate in tough conditions—rain, dirt, sand, and high shock loads. These specially developed chains are used as the part of the drive train to transmit the motor power to the back wheel (Figure 1.19).

Motorcycle Chains are superior to gears, which are in the crank cases, by the ease in adjusting the shaft center distance and the number of teeth of the sprocket. Therefore, you can freely design the motorcycle's reduction ratio taking into account the specifications and the working conditions. In the case of a racing motorcycle, for example, the engine power may be 180 hp, and the chain speed is 1,500 m/min.

Figure 1.19 Motorcycle Chain in Action

Construction and Features

Motorcycle Chains have the same basic construction and sizes (numbers 40, 50, and 60, Table 1.9) as Standard Roller Chains. But they have a special width of inner links. Because of the very demanding working conditions, some

Table 1.9 Motorcycle Chains

40 Class		50 Class		60 Class	
Chain Number	Inside Width (mm)	Chain Number	Inside Width (mm)	Chain Number	Inside Width (mm)
420	6.35	520	6.35	630	9.53
425	7.95*	525	7.95		
428**	7.95*	530	9.53*		

* Same inside width as ANSI Standard Roller Chain.
** Roller diameter differs from ANSI Standard Roller Chain.

Motorcycle Chains have the following special features:
(1) Strength
   Quad-staked riveting on the pin head helps to retain the link plate on the pin. Connecting links are press fit. (Riveted connecting links are also available.) Link plates are thicker (heavy) and the rollers are seamless.
(2) Wear life
   Special coated pins, sintered bushings that are oil impregnated, and seamless bushings with O-rings are used to extend the wear life of the chain.
(3) Resistance to dirt, sand, or mud
   To prevent debris from getting into tight joints, the bushings are extended beyond the inner link plates, and often O-rings are used to seal the chains. This extension and O-rings prevent abrasive material from getting into the chain.
(4) Appearance
   These chains may have special coloring, plating, (gold or silver), or glossy finish on the plates.

Sprockets

Special sprockets are used for these chains. Numbers 425 and 530 sprockets have the same tooth shapes as standard types.

Selection and Handling
(1) Usually the specifications differ for each motorcycle or application, even with the same-sized chains. Do not select the chain just by size of the sprocket; take into account the application. For example, an off-road motorcycle travels through dirt and sand, which will get on the chain. You should avoid the use of oil-impregnated sintered bushings for this application.
(2) Failure of Motorcycle Chains may result in injury or death. Care must be exercised when connecting or aligning the chains.
(3) Both O-ring chains and oil-impregnated sintered bushing chains wear rapidly if the O-rings fall off or if the oil in the sintered bushings is depleted. If either of these situations occur, the chain must be replaced —even if it has not elongated to the limit.

(4) The life of O-ring chain is usually determined by the durability of the O-ring. To improve the durability, there should be an oil film on the O-ring at all times. Even though it is a sealed chain, lubrication is required to extend the working life of the O-ring. Cleaning sprays may cause deterioration of the O-rings. Do not allow chains to air dry after washing, or to rust.

Technical Trend

Motorcycles are getting faster and more powerful. Therefore, Motorcycle Chains must have greater durability. At the same time, motorcycles are getting lighter and smaller. Manufacturers are working on new materials, sizes, and heat treatments to improve the performance of the chain.

1.5.3 Chains for Automotive Engines

Transmission: Camshaft driving, balancer driving

Application Examples

Automotive Chains are used for driving the camshafts in engines, counterbalance shafts, or oil pumps. Some manufacturers use cog belts instead of chains in this application. (See Figure 1.20.)

Camshaft drives transmit the crankshaft rotation to the camshaft of the overhead cam (OHC) engine at a ratio of 2:1. The counterbalance shaft and oil pump are also driven by the crankshaft. Both of these drives are installed inside the engine and are not visible from the outside.

These chains work at the temperature range of -30° to 130°C, and rotate at about 600 to 7,000 rpm. Counterbalance drive sprockets rotate at 1,200 to 14,000 rpm, which is equivalent to a speed of 1,800 m/min.! This is twice the speed of engine drive chain. Motorcycles also use camshaft drives, but this discussion is limited to automobiles that use roller chains, which are usually offered by Japanese or European manufacturers. In the United States, Silent Chains are usually used for camshaft drives in automobiles, but roller chains are being increasingly used.

Figure 1.20   Engine Cutaway to Show Chain Drive

Construction and Features

(1) Single strand chain with a pitch of 9.525 mm or 8.0 mm is usually used. (See Figure 1.21.) In diesel engines or other high-load engines, double strand chains may be used.

(2) The chains are used at high speed. Therefore, the wear between the pins and bushings is the main concern. The surface of the pin is usually hardened with Hmv 1,600 or more.

Figure 1.21 Automotive Drive Chain and Sintered Metal Sprockets

Sprockets
(1) Tooth shapes are either ANSI- or BS-type. Currently the BS-type is used more frequently.
(2) Automotive engines are produced on a large scale. The sprockets for both the crankshaft and the camshaft are mass-produced from sintered metal.

Selection and Handling
(1) These chains are used with chain guides, levers, and tensioners to reduce chain elongation, vibration, and noise.
(2) Generally, the chains are selected according to the transmission torque, small-sprocket speed, and the layout. In mid- to high-speed transmission, vibration and lubrication must also be considered.
(3) These chains need forced lubrication.

Technical Trend
Manufacturers are focusing attention on the following issues:
(1) Making lighter-weight, smaller-sized chains.
(2) Improving reliability of the entire transmission system, including sprockets, guides, levers, and tensioners.
(3) Decreasing noise from the chain, and throughout the entire drive system.

1.6 SPECIALTY CHAINS, TYPE 2

1.6.1 Miniature Chain

Transmission: Office machines and general uses

Application Example

Many users require "smaller, lighter" equipment. The transmission chains for this equipment must also be smaller. Miniature Chains RS11SS (3.7465 mm pitch) and RS15 (4.7625 mm pitch) are designed to fill this request. (See the lower part of Figure 1.22.)

Figure 1.22　Miniature Chain Versus Other Chains

Construction and Features

This is a bushing chain series, which means it does not have rollers. RS11SS is made from 304 stainless steel; RS15 is made from carbon steel. Offset links are not available for Miniature Chains.

Sprockets

There are special sprockets for RS11SS (tooth sizes of 12 through 48) and RS15 (tooth sizes of 11 through 35). Sprockets for RS11SS are made of 304 stainless steel; for RS15 they are carbon steel.

Technical Trend

In the case of small transmissions, toothed belts seem to have advantages over chains.

1.6.2 Leaf Chains

Lifting, counterbalance, forklifts, machine tools

Application Examples

Leaf Chains are used for fork lift masts, as balancers between head and counterweight in machine tools, or for low-speed pulling (tension linkage). This type of chain is also called "Balance Chain," and is regulated by ANSI B29.8M, JIS B 1804, and ISO 4347. (See Figure 1.23.)

Figure 1.23   Leaf Chain and a Leaf Chain Application

Construction and Features

These steel chains have a very simple construction: link plates and pins. The chain number indicates the pitch and the lacing of the links. (See Figure 1.24.) The chains also have the features shown below.

(1) High tensile strength per section area. This allows the design of smaller equipment.

(2) There are A- and B-type chains in this series. Both AL6 Series and BL6 Series have the same chain pitch as RS60 (19.05 mm), but they differ, as shown in Table 1.10.

(3) These chains cannot be driven with sprockets.

Sprockets

Sheaves, not sprockets, are used to change the direction of these chains (Figure 1.25).

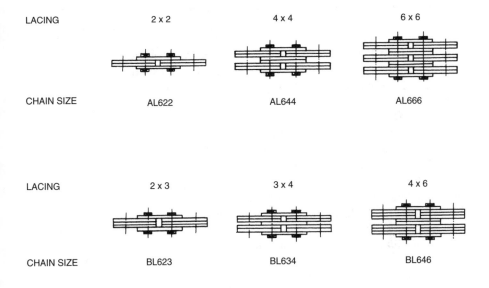

LACING   2 x 2   4 x 4   6 x 6

CHAIN SIZE   AL622   AL644   AL666

LACING   2 x 3   3 x 4   4 x 6

CHAIN SIZE   BL623   BL634   BL646

Figure 1.24 Leaf Chain Lacing Patterns

Table 1.10 Difference Between AL6 Series and BL6 Series

	AL6 Series	**BL6 Series**
Pin Diameter	5.94	7.90
Plate Thickness	2.4	3.2
Plate Height	15.6	18.1
Plate Lacing	2X2, 4X4 Even lacing is standard.	2X3, 3X4 Odd lacing is standard.

Selection and Handling

(1) In roller chains, all the link plates have higher fatigue resistance due to the compressive stress of press fits. In Leaf Chains, only two outer plates are press fit. Therefore, the tensile strength of Leaf Chains is high, but the maximum allowable tension is low. Use safety guards at all times, and be particularly alert to assure that the safety factor is in the manufacturer's catalog. Use extra safety factors where consequences of chain failure are severe.

(2) The more plates used in the lacing, the higher the tensile strength. But this does not improve the maximum allowable tension directly; the number of plates used may be limited.

(3) The pins articulate directly on the plates, and the bearing pressure is very high. The chains need regular lubrication. The use of SAE 30 or 40 machine oil is suggested for most applications.

(4) When the chain speed is greater than 30 m/min., or if the chain is cycled more than 1,000 times in a day, it will wear very quickly, even with lubrication. In either of these cases, use RS Roller Chains.

(5) AL-type should be used only under conditions in which:
   • There are no shock loads.
   • Wear is not a big problem.
   • Number of cycles is less than 100 a day.
   Under other conditions, BL-type should be considered.

(6) If you select a chain using a low safety factor, the stress in parts becomes higher. In this situation, if the chain is used in corrosive conditions, it may fatigue and break very quickly. If you're operating under these conditions, perform maintenance frequently.

(7) The shape of the clevis depends on the type of end link of the chain (outer link or inner link). Manufacturers produce clevis pins or clevis connectors, but typically, the user supplies the clevis (Figures 1.26 and 1.27). The strands should be furnished to length by the manufacturer. An incorrectly made clevis may reduce the working life of the chain. Contact the manufacturer or refer to the ANSI standard.

(8) The sheaves are usually supplied by the user.

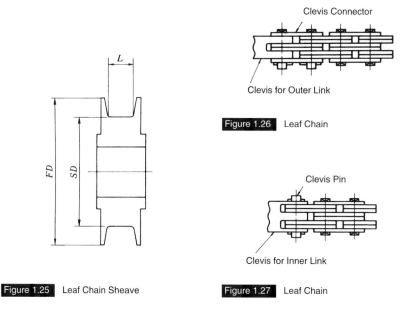

Clevis Connector

Clevis for Outer Link

Figure 1.26   Leaf Chain

Clevis Pin

Clevis for Inner Link

Figure 1.25   Leaf Chain Sheave

Figure 1.27   Leaf Chain

1.6.3 Inverted Tooth Chain (Silent Chain)

Transmission

Application Example

Silent Chains are used for the camshaft drive of the mid- to large-size motorcycle engines and automobile engines in the United States, the transfer-case drive in four-wheel-drive vehicles, and the primary drive between the engine and transmission, as well as in other high-speed applications (Figure 1.28).

Figure 1.28 Silent Chain

Construction and Features

(1) Silent Chains have a very simple construction: only plates and pins. Today's Silent Chains are actually an update of a 19th-century design. ANSI B29.2M-1982 regulates the standard pitch, width, and kilowatt ratings of the chains and sprockets.

(2) There are eight different pitches from 9.52 mm to 50.8 mm.

(3) The link plate receives tension and has a notch for engaging the sprockets. There is no notch on the guide plate. These plates act as guides for the sprockets.

(4) Pins may be round or have other shapes, such as D-shape (Figure 1.29).

(5) All of the chain components share the tension. Silent Chains have higher capacity than roller chains of the same width.

(6) Because the link plates of Silent Chain strike the sprocket at an angle, the impact and the noise are reduced (Figure 1.30). This is why these chains are called "silent." The higher the chain speed, the greater the difference from roller chains.

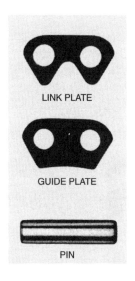

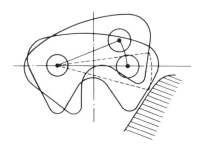

Figure 1.29   Silent Chain Components

Figure 1.30   Silent Chain Strikes the Sprocket at an Angle, Reducing Noise

Sprockets

The sprocket for Silent Chain is shaped like a gear. In the ANSI standard, the tooth working face is a straight line. But in HY-VO® Chains (see Applications Series below), an involute tooth is used for the sprocket.

Selection and Handling

(1) Silent Chains are good for high-speed transmission.

(2) If single- or multiple-strand roller chains are an option, they are less expensive. Wider Silent Chain becomes relatively competitive in price.

(3) Silent Chains must be lubricated during operation. Use an oil bath if the speed is less than 600 m/min. If the speed is more than 600 m/min., or if the shaft center distance is short, use a pump or forced lubrication. Silent Chains wear rapidly without lubrication.

(4) The notch on the plates can engage with the sprockets from only one direction. The chain is not for reversing applications.

(5) To select the right Silent Chain for your operation, refer to the manufacturer's catalog.

Application Series

HY-VO® Chain is a unique type of Silent Chain. HY-VO stands for H̲IGH
CAPACIT̲Y̲, H̲IGH VELOCIT̲Y̲, and INV̲O̲LUTE TOOTH, and it is a registered
trademark of Borg-Warner Automotive, Inc.

In Silent Chain, the pin and the plate rotate against each other. In HY-VO
Chains, the pin is comprised of two pieces that have rotational contact. Due to
the rotational contact of the pins, the wear life of the chain is increased. Also
in HY-VO Chains, the contact point between the pins moves up when the
chain engages the sprocket (Figure 1.31). This construction decreases chordal
action (which was discussed in Basics Section 2.2.1), vibration, and noise.

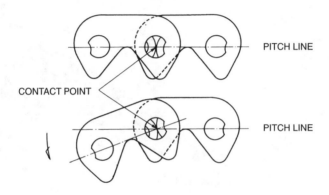

Figure 1.31   HY-VO Chain

2 . SMALL PITCH CONVEYOR CHAINS

Small pitch conveyor chain is based on ANSI Roller Chains with attachments added to make them suitable for conveyor uses (Figure 2.1). There are many types of small pitch conveyor chains. Figure 2.2 shows the relationship between these chains and available options, such as lubrication free or environmentally resistant.

Figure 2.1   Attachment Chains

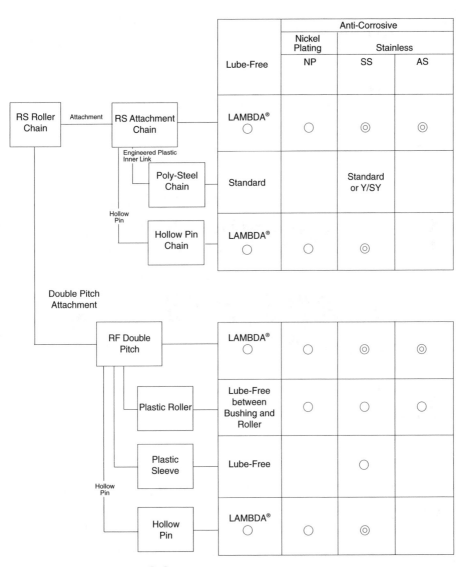

		Anti-Corrosive		
		Nickel Plating	Stainless	
	Lube-Free	NP	SS	AS
RS Attachment Chain	LAMBDA® ○	○	◎	◎
Poly-Steel Chain	Standard		Standard or Y/SY	
Hollow Pin Chain	LAMBDA® ○	○	◎	
RF Double Pitch	LAMBDA® ○	○	◎	◎
Plastic Roller	Lube-Free between Bushing and Roller	○	○	○
Plastic Sleeve	Lube-Free		○	
Hollow Pin	LAMBDA® ○	○	◎	

RS Roller Chain — Attachment — RS Attachment Chain
Engineered Plastic Inner Link
Hollow Pin
Double Pitch Attachment

NOTE: 1) ○, ◎ Available.
2) ◎ Heat resistant from -20°~400°C. Consult chain manufacturer in case temperature exceeds these limits.
3) AS Pins and bushings are precipitation-hardened. All others are 304 stainless.

Figure 2.2   The Relationship Among Chains and Their Availability

125

2.1 SMALL PITCH CONVEYOR CHAINS FOR GENERAL USE

2.1.1 RS Attachment Chain

Light conveyance: General uses

Application Example

RS Attachment Chain is used for short conveyors (usually less than 10 m) of small products. This chain is also suitable for conditions under which noise should be avoided (Figure 2.3).

Figure 2.3 RS Attachment Chains

Table 2.1 Standard Dimensions for RS Attachment Chain[1]

Chain No.	Pitch (mm)	Maximum Allowable Tension (kN)	Note[2]
25	6.35	0.64	Bushed
35	9.525	1.52	Bushed
40	12.70	2.65	
50	15.875	4.31	
60	19.05	6.27	
80	25.40	10.6	
100	31.75	17.1	
120	38.10	23.9	
140	44.45	32.3	
160	50.80	40.9	

[1]These dimensions are from Tsubaki. Other manufacturers' products may vary.
[2]Bushed chain is designed without a roller.

Construction and Features

This chain is based on Standard RS Roller Chain with added attachments for conveyance, as indicated in ANSI B29.1 for reference.

Table 2.1 shows the chain size, pitch, and maximum allowable tension for standard products from Tsubaki. Among these chains, Numbers 40, 50, 60, and 80 are used most frequently.

The features are shown below:

(1) Due to the small pitch of these chains, the drive design is smaller.
(2) Usually sprockets with a large number of teeth are used. Therefore, the chain speed does not vary significantly, and the chain engages with sprockets with less noise.
(3) These chains may be used for high-speed conveyors.
(4) A wide variety of standard attachments and special attachments (Plus α Alpha series) are available for this chain series.
(5) Slip-fit, spring-clip type connecting links are provided for RS40, RS50, and RS60 chains. RS80 has cottered connecting links.

Sprockets

Standard RS Roller Chain sprockets are used with these chains.

Selection and Handling

(1) If the attachments receive large bending or twisting forces, make sure the chain has adequate strength. In these conditions, Double Pitch Roller Chain or a chain with larger pitch will be more effective; both have larger attachments.
(2) Due to light weight, the chain inertia is smaller.
(3) The tolerance of the overall chain length is -0.05 to 0.25 percent (JIS Standard) of the standard length. This is greater than that of RS Roller Chain.
(4) In these chains, the clearance between the parts is small. Chain articulation is easily affected by dirt or contamination in the joints.

Application Series

(1) Lubrication free: LAMBDA® series (operating temperature of -10° to 60°C).
(2) Environmentally resistant: Special coatings or base materials may be used to add extra resistance. These include:
• Coating: Nickel plating, WP® specification.
• Material: 304 stainless steel SS-type, AS-type with the pins, bushings, and rollers made of precipitation-hardened stainless steel and the other components the same material as SS-type.

2.1.2 Double Pitch Roller Chain

Light conveyance: General uses

Application Example

This is the most commonly used conveyor chain and is utilized widely in the auto parts, electric, electronic, and precision machinery industries (Figure 2.4).

| Figure 2.4 | Double Pitch Roller Chain |

Construction and Features

Double Pitch Roller Chain has the same basic construction as Standard Roller Chain, but double pitch means the chain pitch is twice as long, has flat-shaped link plates, and longer attachments. This series is regulated by ANSI B29.4, ISO 1275-A, and JIS B 1803. Table 2.2 shows the size, pitch, and maximum allowable tension for standard specification Double Pitch Roller Chain.

Among these, four sizes—Numbers 2040, 2050, 2060, and 2080—are most commonly used. The features are shown below:

(1) Double Pitch Roller Chains have the smallest tolerances for overall length compared to all other types of conveyor chains.
Without attachments: 0 to +0.15 percent of the nominal chain length.
With attachments: 0 to +0.25 percent of the nominal chain length.

Table 2.2 Dimensions of Double Pitch Roller Chain[1]

Chain No.	Pitch (mm)	Maximum Allowable Load (kN)
2040	25.40	2.65
2050	31.75	4.31
2060	38.10	6.27
2080	50.80	10.6
2100	63.50	17.1
2120	76.20	23.9
2160	101.60	40.9

[1] These dimensions are from Tsubaki. Other manufacturers' products may vary.

(2) There are two types of rollers, R-roller (oversized) and S-roller (standard). The S-rollers are used in short-length and slow-speed conveyance. The R-rollers are most commonly used, especially for longer conveyors.

(3) There are many standard attachments and special attachments (Plus α Alpha series) available for this series.

(4) Chains sized 2060 and larger have greater rigidity than Standard RS Attachment Chains because the link plates are one size thicker (heavy).

(5) Due to its light weight, the chain's inertia is smaller.

(6) Slip-fit, spring-clip-type connecting links are provided for Numbers 2040, 2050, and 2060. Number 2080 has cottered connecting links.

Sprockets

Special sprockets are required for these chains. For the S-rollers, standard sprockets exceeding 30 teeth are used (30-tooth sprocket has 15 effective teeth). The chain engages every second tooth.

Selection and Handling

(1) Double Pitch Roller Chains are selected according to the allowable roller load and maximum allowable tension.

(2) When the attachments receive a large bending or twisting force, make sure the chain has adequate strength. In these cases, a larger-pitch roller chain is frequently used because it has a thicker plate and longer attachment.

(3) In these chains, clearance between the components is small. Chain articulation is easily affected by dirt or contamination in the joints.

Application Series

(1) Lubrication-free: LAMBDA® series (operating temperature of -10° to 150°C). O-ring chains are also lubrication-free chains, however, they have bending resistance and sometimes, after engaging the sprockets, the chains retain the articulated position. This may occur at the return side of the chain loop. Therefore, O-ring chains are not suitable for conveyance.

(2) Environmentally resistant: Special coatings or base materials may be used to add extra resistance.
   • Coating: Nickel plating, WP® specification.
   • Material: 304 stainless steel SS-type and AS-type with pins, bushings, and small rollers are made of precipitation-hardened stainless steel.

2.1.3 Plastic Roller Plus Plastic Sleeve Chain

Transmission, conveyance: Maintenance-free type, general uses

Application Example

Plastic Sleeve Chain is used for general purpose with small loads, and under conditions that require maintenance-free or low-noise applications.

Construction and Features

In Plastic Sleeve Chains, the pins and bushings are separated by a sleeve made of self-lubricating engineered plastic. This feature makes the chains maintenance free (Figures 2.5 and 2.6).

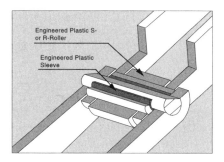

Figure 2.5   Plastic Sleeve Chain

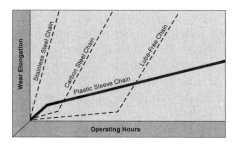

Figure 2.6   Plastic Sleeve Chain Versus Other Chains

This chain has the features shown below:
(1) A small coefficient of friction (R-Roller): 0.08 versus 0.12 for all-steel chain.
(2) Light weight: 30 percent less than the weight of all-steel chain with R-rollers.

(3) Low noise: the noise made from engaging the sprockets is 5 to 7 dB lower.
(4) In Plastic Sleeve Chain, the maximum allowable tension is one-sixth, and the allowable load of the R-roller is about one-third that of the same-sized all-steel chain (with lubrication).

Sprockets

Use the same sprockets as for Double Pitch Roller Chain.

Application Series

There are special low-noise engineered plastic R-rollers, which can reduce the noise from the standard engineered plastic type by 7 dB. The allowable roller load for low-noise R-rollers is about 30 percent less than standard engineered plastic R-rollers.

2.1.4 Hollow Pin Chain

Conveyance, simplified attachment installation, general uses

Construction and Features

In Hollow Pin Chain, the pin has a hole, allowing for the installation of various attachments (Figure 2.7). Usually these chains are used for conveyors (Figure 2.8). Sizes are shown in Tables 2.3 and 2.4.

The advantages of installing attachments into the hollow pin include the following:

(1) The hollow pin is at the center of articulation, and always keeps the pitch length. Regardless of whether the chain is straight or wrapping around the sprocket, the center distance of attachments is always the same. Figure 2.8 shows an example of installing a mesh net. Even when the chains bend, the mesh net does not expand or contract.

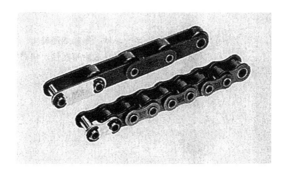

Figure 2.7   Hollow Pin Chain

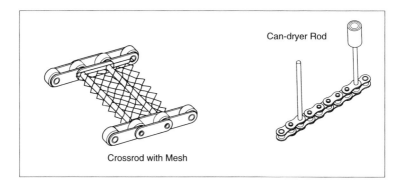

Can-dryer Rod

Crossrod with Mesh

Figure 2.8   Installing Attachments

(2) With a crossrod over two chains, the load from the attachments is distributed to both sides of plates equally. The chain can fully use its strength and not twist.

(3) It is easy to change, maintain, and adjust attachments.

Sprockets

Standard sprockets are used for the small pitch series. For double pitch series, standard sprockets for Double Pitch Roller Chain are used.

Selection and Handling

(1) These chains are selected using the same methods as other conveyor chains. Care must be taken since the maximum allowable tension of hollow pin chains is less than that of the same-sized standard chains.

(2) Retaining rings are used on the pin head for connecting links. When an attachment link is to be added to an HP connecting link, the attachment link pin must be longer than those used in the rest of the chain.

(3) The pin is not riveted in this chain. The lower maximum allowable load and the high rigidity of the pin make it difficult for the link plates to come off.

(4) The small pitch series and the S-roller (standard) types in the double pitch series are bushing chains, which do not have rollers.

Table 2.3 Sizes for Hollow Pin Chain[1]

Chain No.	Pitch	Pin Minimum Inner Diameter (mm)	Maximum Allowable Load (kN)
RS40HP	12.70	4.00	1.76
RS50HP	15.875	5.12	3.14
RS60HP	19.05	5.99	4.21
RS80HP	25.40	8.02	7.64

[1]These dimensions are from Tsubaki. Other manufacturers' products may vary.

Table 2.4 Sizes for Double Pitch Hollow Pin Chain[1]

Chain No.	Pitch	Pin Minimum Inner Diameter (mm)	Maximum Allowable Load (kN)
RF2040HP	25.40	4.00	1.76
RF2050HP	31.75	5.12	3.14
RF2060HP	38.10	5.99	4.21
RF2080HP	50.80	8.02	7.64

[1]These dimensions are from Tsubaki. Other manufacturers' products may vary.

2.2 SPECIALTY CHAINS

2.2.1 Step (Escalator) Chain

Small size conveyance: Escalator

Application Example

Step Chain, which is also called Escalator Chain, moves the steps on escalators or drives moving sidewalks (Figure 2.9).

Figure 2.9   Step (Escalator) Chain

Construction and Features

In escalators, the steps are installed about every 400 mm, however, widths and heights are different. The tensile strength of step chains ranges from 6 to 30 tons. The 9-ton type and 15-ton type are most common.

The chain pitch should be as small as possible to reduce the effects of chordal action, which is caused by the chain/sprocket engagement. Using the smallest size possible allows the chain to operate more smoothly (Table 2.5).

The way steps are installed on chains differs from country to country. In Japan, the bearing part is in the center of the chain plate, so the step shaft is installed there. In other countries, extended pins are used as the shaft for the step (Figure 2.10).

Table 2.5 Pitch and Attachment Spacing for Step (Elevator) Chain

	Pitch (mm)	Attachment Spacing
Small Size	67.7	6th
Medium Size	81.3	5th
Large Size	101.6	4th

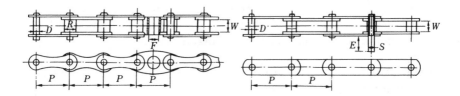

Figure 2.10 Bearing Hole and Extended Pin on Step (Escalator) Chain

Usually rollers on the step side carry the weight of steps and passengers, but in some types the chain rollers carry the weight.

The features of step chain are:

(1) Greater wear resistance. The pin diameter is larger than standard chains.

(2) Length from step to step and from chain to chain is strictly controlled.

Sprockets

Special sprockets are required for step chains.

Technical Trends

The chains shown above are being adapted for the following:

(1) Lubrication-free type. (However, lubrication is mandated at regular intervals.)

(2) Low-noise type (for quiet environments).

2.2.2 ATC Chain

Small conveyance: Machine tools

Application Example

ATC Chain is used to organize tools in the automatic tool changer, which is a device on Computer Numeric Control (CNC) machine tools.

When fewer than 30 tools are used, the tool pots are mounted on a disc. Tools are changed by controlling the disc. When more than 30 tools are used, tool pots are mounted directly on the chain. (See Figures 2.11 through 2.13.)

Comparing the disc and chain set-ups, differences include the following points:

(1) Using the same area, the chain type can have as much as 1.5 times as many tools as that of the disc (Figure 2.13).

(2) To add tools to the disc type, you must change to a larger-diameter disc and redesign the changer. But with the chain type, you simply add chain strands. The changer location remains the same, allowing standardization. (See Figure 2.14.)

HP-Type

SK-Type

Figure 2.11   ATC Chain Can Accomodate Many Tools

Figure 2.12   ATC Chain

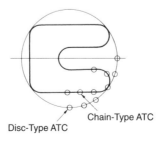

Chain-Type ATC

Disc-Type ATC

Figure 2.13   Chain-Type ATC Can Have 1.5 Times that of Disc-Type ATC

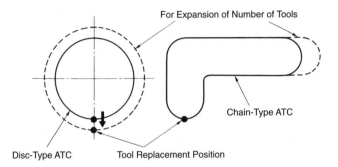

For Expansion of Number of Tools

Chain-Type ATC

Disc-Type ATC

Tool Replacement Position

Figure 2.14 Ways to Add Tools

Construction and Features

There are two types of ATC Chains: SK and HP. Note the following features:

SK series has two strands of chain in which the pitch of the outer link and inner link is different. SK attachments are placed on every other link. There are three standard tool pitches: 95.25, 114.30, and 133.35 mm, which are based on RS100, 120, and 140 transmission chains, respectively. The SK series can bend in only one direction.

HP series has large-diameter hollow pins. There are five standard tool pitches: 90, 100, 130, 140, and 160 mm. HP series can bend in both directions, which permits more freedom in design.

Both types of chain are available for any shank number, including 40 and 50 in MAS, ANSI, and ISO types. Special ATC Chains are also available for 25, 30, 35, 45, and 60; check with the manufacturer.

Sprockets

The SK series ATC Chain uses the sprockets that are used for duplex power transmission roller chain. (The tooth range is limited.) HP series ATC Chain requires special sprockets.

Selection and Handling

(1) ATC Chains must be lubricated.
(2) When there is excessive tool overhang, use a tool guide to keep the chain straight.
(3) Change tools at the position shown in Figure 2.15.
(4) Positioning pins and grippers help to maintain accurate placement.

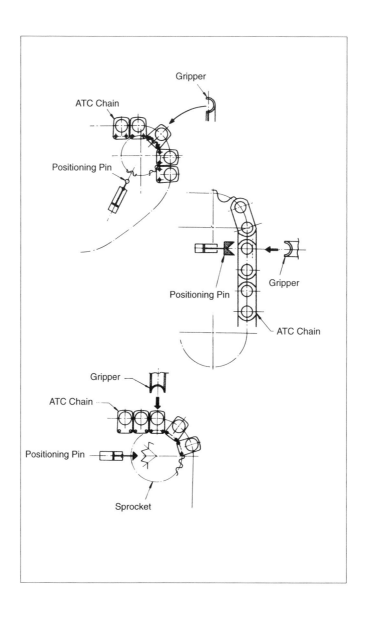

Figure 2.15 Positions for ATC Tool Changers

2.3 Standard Attachments

Most applications use small pitch conveyor chains with attachments in one of these ways:
- Convey materials directly on chain attachments.
- Convey materials on jigs installed on the attachments.

The characteristics of the conveyed materials and the working environment are different for each application. Many types of attachments with and without jigs are available.

There are many different types of attachments; it would be difficult for chain manufacturers to satisfy all customer requirements for quality, price, and delivery if every type of special attachment chain were made. There are too many variations. Chain manufacturers need mass production to maintain high quality, reasonable prices, and quick delivery, not small production lots of many different items.

Current standard attachments are established and selected based upon the long history of attachment chain use and demand, and they provide high quality, economy, and quick delivery to meet the majority of customers' requirements. For small pitch conveyor chains, standard attachments include: A, K, SA, SK, D-1, and D-3 types.

Standard attachments are available for a wide variety of chains:
- With special surface treatments (nickel-plated or WP®).
- Made of 304 stainless steel or other metals.
- For lube-free operations (LAMBDA® series, etc.).

In the following sections, we will explain each standard attachment.

2.3.1 A Attachment

An A attachment is most commonly used. It has a bent link plate that extends out on one side of the chain, forming an L-shape. It comes with one or two bolt holes, which are referenced A-1 or A-2, respectively (Figure 2.16). The attachment interval can vary (for example, on each chain link, every five links, or two attachments in a series with intervals every four links, etc.). Generally two strands of chains with slats are used (Figure 2.17).

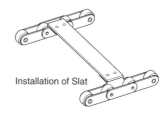

Installation of Slat

Figure 2.16 A-2 Attachment

Figure 2.17 A-2 Attachment with Slat

Attachments are subjected to bending force. If they convey heavy objects, have long jigs installed, or receive side loads, twisting force is added to the bending force. Depending on the application, make sure you consider these forces in your calculations.

The shape of the attachment influences the design of the equipment. If slats do not cover the chain rollers, guide rails may be used to support the chain rollers on the return side.

2.3.2 K Attachment

This is an attachment made by installing A attachments on both sides of the chain. The attachment is called K-1 or K-2 based on the number of bolt holes on one side. The attachment interval can vary the same as the A attachment (Figure 2.18).

Figure 2.18 K-1 Attachment

The top of the attachment is higher than the R-rollers, so slats or jigs can be installed over the chains (Figure 2.19). Objects can also be conveyed directly on the K attachments.

NOTE: When the bushings and rollers wear extensively, the upper side of the rollers may touch the slats or jigs. Larger than standard over-sized rollers or flanged F-rollers may cause interference with the slat or jigs. Please check with the chain manufacturer.

When a wide slat is installed on two A attachment chains, the slats may not be able to support the weight. A chain with K attachments is installed between the A attachment chains to help support the load (Figure 2.20).

When the slats are rigid enough and are fastened well to the attachments, there is almost no effect from bending force to the strength of the attachment. But if the slat is not fastened well, make sure to consider the bending force in your calculation.

If long jigs are installed, or the attachment receives side loads, it is exposed to twisting forces.

The return side of the K attachment chain cannot be supported with guide rails on the rollers. The return may be slack or supported in some other way (Figure 2.21).

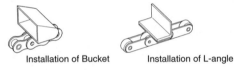

Installation of Bucket   Installation of L-angle

Figure 2.19 K Attachment with Jigs

Take-up

Drive

Figure 2.20 Using A and K Attachments

Figure 2.21 K Attachment Configuration (Note return side.)

2.3.3 SA Attachment

For the SA attachment, the link plate is extended on one side of the chain, and one or two bolt holes are installed. These are called SA-1 or SA-2 depending on the number of bolt holes (Figure 2.22). The attachment interval can vary the same as the A attachment. These attachments may be adapted for use with hooks or slats (Figure 2.23).

The SA attachment is simpler and stronger than the A attachment, and may receive bending and twisting force depending on the direction of the loads.

The return side of the chains can be supported by guide rails on the rollers unless bolts extend into the attachment.

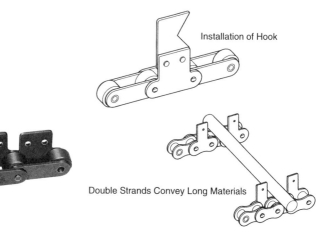

Installation of Hook

Double Strands Convey Long Materials

Figure 2.22   SA-2 Attachment

Figure 2.23   SA Attachments Are Adaptable for Use with Hooks or Slats

2.3.4 SK Attachment

SK attachments are made by installing SA attachments on both sides of the chain. They are called SK-1 or SK-2, depending on the number of bolt holes on one side. The attachment interval can vary the same as the A attachment (Figure 2.24).

Usually SK attachments are used with dogs or jigs (Figure 2.25). SK attachments are strong enough to stand up to bending or twisting forces.

The return side of SK attachment chains cannot be supported by guide rails on the rollers like A or SA attachment chains. The return must be slack or supported in some other manner.

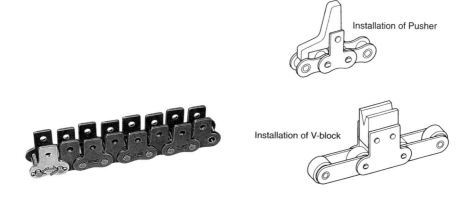

Installation of Pusher

Installation of V-block

Figure 2.24   SK-1 Attachments

Figure 2.25   SK Attachments May Be Used with Dogs or Jigs

2.3.5 D Attachment (Extended Pin)

In this form, the one end of the pin is extended. The attachment interval can vary the same as the A attachment (Figure 2.26).

As shown in Figure 2.27, two sets of D attachment chains can be connected to crossrods, or jigs (such as blocks) may be installed.

The extended pins are subjected to bending and shearing forces. The allowable load of D attachment that is shown in a manufacturer's catalog is based on a bending force concentrated at the center of the extended pin.

The return side of the D attachment chain can be supported by guide rails on the rollers.

Figure 2.26   D-3 Attachment (Extended Pin)

Figure 2.27   D Attachments with Crossrods and Jigs

2.4 Plus α Alpha Attachments

Plus α Alpha attachments are the second most frequently used type of modified attachments. These attachments are sorted into three types:
 (1) Hole diameter in an A or K attachment or the length
    of the pin in a D attachment (Figures 2.28 and 2.29).
 (2) Installing a nut in the hole of an A or K attachment (Figure 2.30).
 (3) Using a different type of attachment (Figures 2.31 (i) and (ii)).

Types (1) and (2) are easy-to-order products. Type (3) includes special designs that are available for the convenience of equipment designers. These designs can be used whenever possible for equipment.

Plus α Alpha attachments are available in the following types of chains:
 (1) Special surface treatment (nickel-plated, WP®).
 (2) Made of 304 stainless steel or other metals.
 (3) Lube-free (LAMBDA® series or other type).

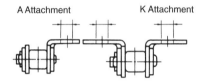

| Figure 2.28 | Changing the Hole Diameter in A or K Attachments |

| Figure 2.29 | Changing the Pin Length in D Attachments |

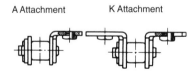

| Figure 2.30 | Installing a Nut in an A or K Attachment |

	Attachment Series (1)					
Type	Ground attachment. 	Large chain attachment (over RS180). 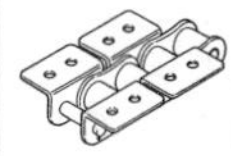	Double pitch with deep link. 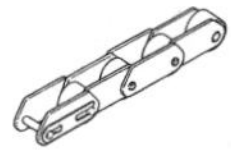	Internally bent attachment. 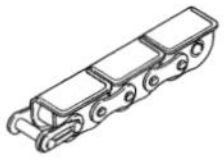	Hollow pin with attachment. 	Curved attachment with guide plate. 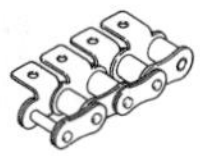
Symbol	PG	RS	RFD	UM	HP	GP
Spec	The upper surface of the link plate has been ground to provide a smooth con-veying surface.	Attachment for larger sizes over RS180.	Side plate is higher than the top of the roller.	Inner bent attachments are chamfered to protect conveyed materials.	HP chain with attachment.	Curved chain with attachment and guide plate.
	Attachment Series (2)					
Type	Triangle attachment. 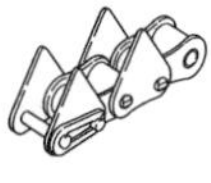	Sticker attachment. 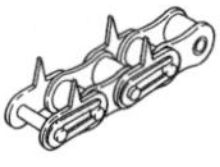	Bushing attachment. 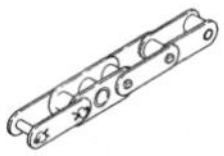	Grip attachment. 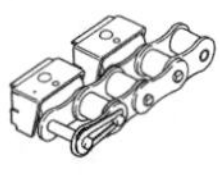	No-bend attachment. 	Rubber attachment. 
Symbol	RE	FS	AB	KU	NB	RSG
Spec	Conveying bar-type objects.	Sharp-top attachment is ideal for conveying board-type objects.	Press-fitted bushing is ideal for bearing.	Gripping attachment for thin objects, such as film.	The chain bends in one direction only.	Rubber pads hold the conveyed material from above and below.
	Top Plate, Slat Attachment					
Type	Rubber pad. 	Heat-treated top plate. 	Bent-end top plate. 	Inclined top plate. 	Crescent plate. 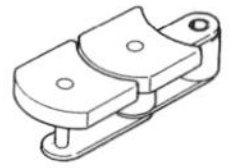	Slat attachment. 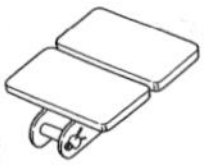
Symbol	PSG	YP	SM	CT	CL	SLT
Spec	Rubber pads prevent damage to the conveyed materials.	Improved wear resistance.	Easy lateral transfer of conveyed objects.	Smaller gap between the plates.	For bottling and canning industries.	Excellent for conveying relatively heavy goods.

Figure 2.31 (i) Other Types of Attachments

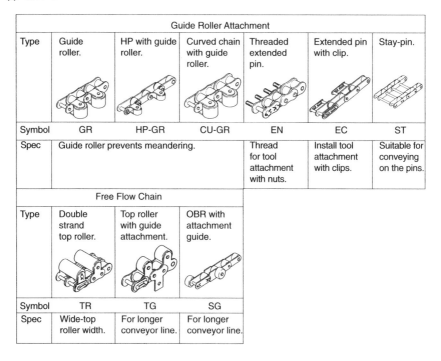

Guide Roller Attachment						
Type	Guide roller.	HP with guide roller.	Curved chain with guide roller.	Threaded extended pin.	Extended pin with clip.	Stay-pin.
Symbol	GR	HP-GR	CU-GR	EN	EC	ST
Spec	Guide roller prevents meandering.			Thread for tool attachment with nuts.	Install tool attachment with clips.	Suitable for conveying on the pins.

Free Flow Chain		
Type	Double strand top roller.	Top roller with guide attachment.	OBR with attachment guide.
Symbol	TR	TG	SG
Spec	Wide-top roller width.	For longer conveyor line.	For longer conveyor line.

Figure 2.31 (ii) Other Types of Attachments

2.5 Special Attachments

These made-to-order products require careful consideration. Should a manufacturer supply them, or should you make them in house? Here are some points to weigh:

High Accuracy

The most common requirement is the height from the guide rail to the upper edge of the A or K attachment. The "ground upper surface" type of Plus α Alpha attachments has high accuracy. The tolerance is approximately 0.2 mm, depending on the chain size and manufacturer. For standard attachments, the tolerance range is wider: about two to three times that of the Plus α Alpha attachments. During normal service, the chain will wear, and the height will change.

If you require greater accuracy than is available from Plus α Alpha attachments, make a shuttle that supports the conveyed objects, and use chains only for tracking.

When you need high accuracy in other dimensions besides height, contact the chain manufacturer.

Cost

The reason chain manufacturers can produce attachments at low cost is that they use a punch-press process, which is efficient but takes time to set up. To absorb the cost of set-up, parts need to be produced in large quantity: hundreds of pieces. (The smaller the part, the more parts needed to offset the set-up costs.)

If you need a special attachment in low quantities, the chain manufacturer can help work out a design that can be produced at lower cost.

Turnaround Time

Chain manufacturers can supply almost all the standard attachments from stock. Special order attachments require lead times. The lead time for specialty attachments runs from several weeks to several months. To prevent a crisis situation, in the event of normal wear or catastrophic failure, you should stock replacement chain and re-order well in advance. Figure 2.32 shows several examples of specialty attachment chains that can be made.

Applications

Figure 2.32 Specialty Attachments

3. PRECISION CONVEYOR CHAINS

Times have changed. In the old days, most accurate indexing drives used a turntable or pushing transfer. But these designs have limits on the number of station installations and starting and stopping cycles (Figure 3.1).

In the 1980s, Precision Conveyor Chains were developed for this application. These chains do not wear or elongate, which were the major obstacles to chains in accurate indexing drives. In addition, the number of stations is limited only by the practical length of the chain. And there is more freedom in the starting and stopping cycle, because the chain can be connected in a series (Figure 3.2).

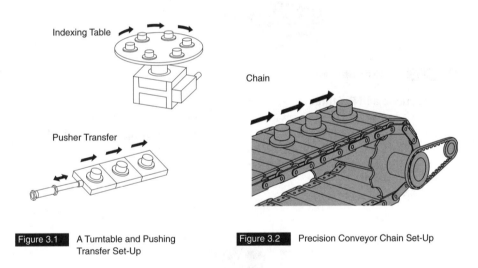

Figure 3.1	A Turntable and Pushing Transfer Set-Up

Figure 3.2	Precision Conveyor Chain Set-Up

3.1 Bearing Bush Chain

Light to heavy conveyance: No elongation, electric, electronic, precision machinery industries

Application Examples

Bearing Bush Chain (Figure 3.3) is used in automatic assembling, packaging, filling, and parts installation for a variety of industries, including electric, electronic, semiconductor, automobile, and food as well as in other precision machinery. It includes the following features:

(1) High accuracy and no elongation.
(2) Interchangeability with other double pitch roller chains and large pitch conveyor chains.
(3) Low cost.

Figure 3.3   Bearing Bush Chain

Constructions and Features

Usually chains are designed with gaps between the pins and bushings for proper operation. With Bearing Bush Chain, needle bearings are installed between the pins and bushings. These add rolling elements between these components and eliminate the sliding friction (Figure 3.4).

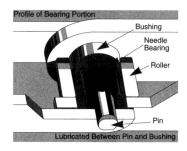

Figure 3.4   Needle Bearings in Precision Chain

The advantages of this design include:

(1) Immediately after installation, the chain stretches a little (less than 0.03 percent) to fit the contacting surface of chain parts. After that, it doesn't stretch (Figure 3.5). The results include the following points:

i) Accurate positioning in a high-speed or indexing drive. For example, in an application of automatic installation of electronic parts with 30 stations, a conveying speed of 10 m/min., and an index of 0.6 seconds, the positioning accuracy is ± 0.2 mm (using a positioning pin).

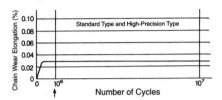

Figure 3.5 After Installation, Precision Chain Has No Elongation

ii) No annoying position-adjustment maintenance.
iii) No take-up adjustment or lubrication.

(2) The main dimensions are the same as double pitch roller chain and large pitch conveyor chain (R-rollers). That gives you the following benefits:

i) Change from standard chains to Bearing Bush Chains with minimal redesign of the equipment.
ii) Low-cost standard sprockets can be used (special made-to-order sprockets are required for high accuracy).
iii) Available with a variety of attachments.

(3) Relatively low cost.

Bearing Bush Chain has many sizes from small to large (Table 3.1).

Sprockets

For double pitch roller chain type, standard sprockets are used for general applications. When the application requires high accuracy, special-order sprockets are needed.

For Engineering Class conveyor chains, machined-tooth sprockets (made to order) are used instead of standard flame-cut sprockets.

Table 3.1 Precision Conveyor Chain

Double Pitch Chain Chain No.	Maximum Allowable Load (kN)	Engineering Class Chain Chain No.	Maximum Allowable Load (kN)
RFN2040R	0.78	RFN03075R	2.45
RFN2050R	1.27	RFN05100R	4.90
RFN2060R	1.76	RFN10150R	7.85
RFN2080R	2.94	RFN12200R	9.81
		RFN17200R	12.70
		RFN26250R	19.60
		RFN36300R	24.50

Points of Selection and Handling

(1) In Bearing Bush Chain, the contacting surfaces between pins and needles or needles and bushings are small. If these parts are subjected to a load larger than the allowable static load of the needle bearing, permanent deformation will occur, and the chain will not operate correctly. The chain tension, including inertia, should be lower than the rated allowable load.

(2) Due to the low bending resistance, the chains will vibrate at the low-tension return side. Guide rails or guide rollers help to prevent vibration.

(3) A "high-precision type," which is more accurate in the overall chain length and the dimension of attachments, is available.

(4) The double pitch chain type is basically an inch-pitch series, but there are some metric pitches available.

Application Series

Link plates of Bearing Bush Chain are nickel-plated to avoid rusting in indoor use.

Stainless steel Bearing Bush Chain is available for corrosive conditions. However, the allowable load is limited because of the low hardness of the contacting parts. In addition, the chain will elongate gradually (Figure 3.6).

Heat-resistant Bearing Bush Chain is available for temperatures up to 150°C.

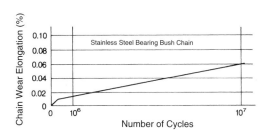

Figure 3.6   Elongation of Stainless Steel Precision Chain

3.2 Indexing Table Chain

Precision conveyance: High accuracy, no elongation
Electric, electronic, and precision machinery industries

Application Examples

Indexing Table Chain is used when you need a more accurate conveyance than Bearing Bush Chain, for example, in an assembling machine with 46 stations, a speed of 10 m/min., an index of 1.0 second, and a stopping accuracy of ± 0.15 mm.

Construction and Features

Indexing Table Chain is expensive because each link has seven needle bearings (Figure 3.7). This chain includes the following features:
(1) No elongation.
(2) Each part is measured with precision; the installing accuracy is ± 0.1 mm.
(3) The chain pitch is indicated in millimeters.
(4) Four sizes are standard: 50 to 150 mm with a maximum allowable tension between 0.49 and 1.27 kN.

Sprockets

Special sprockets with 8 or 12 teeth are required.

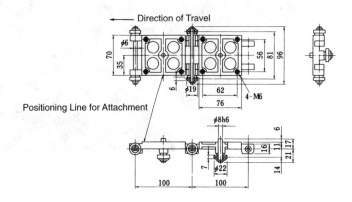

Figure 3.7   Indexing Table Chain

4. TOP CHAINS

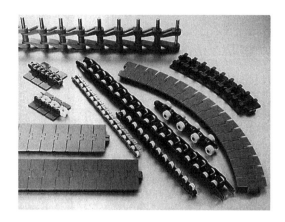

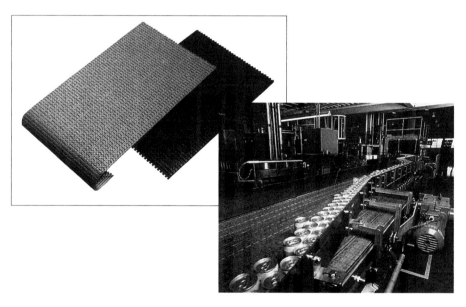

Figure 4.1　Top Chains

4.1 What Is Top Chain?

Top Chain has a plate to hold conveyed objects on its upper side. These chains were originally used for bottling and canning in the food industries. Today you will find them in a variety of applications, because they are convenient and economical (Figure 4.1).

Top Chains are divided into two categories based on the type of movement: linear or curved. The chain may be constructed of engineered plastic, carbon steel, or stainless steel. Usually steel chains have stainless steel top plates; however, engineered plastic snap-on tops are sometimes used.

There are several forms of Top Chains. Figure 4.2 shows the correlation between these chains. There are additional types of chains that are not illustrated in Figure 4.2. These include the following:

- TO type: Steel chains for horizontal circular conveyance.
- TU type: Steel for universal movement.
- TN type (linear conveyance) and TNU type (curved conveyance): Steel chains with snap-on top plates made of engineered plastic.
- RS40P type, RS60P type: Small pitch chains made of engineered plastic.
- RS60P-2 type, RS60PU-2 type: Double strand plastic chains.
- Bel-Top Chain type: Small pitch, wide chain, which is closer in form to a belt than to standard-type chain.

In the following section, we will look at the features and characteristics of Top Chains.

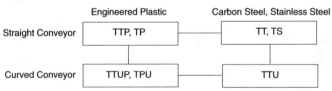

	Engineered Plastic	Carbon Steel, Stainless Steel
Straight Conveyor	TTP, TP	TT, TS
Curved Conveyor	TTUP, TPU	TTU

Figure 4.2   Relationship Between Different Types of Top Chains

4.1.1 Plastic Materials for Top Chains

Most Engineered Plastic Top Chains have molded parts; the pins are made of 304 stainless steel. They offer quiet operation, do not require additional lubrication, and do not scratch conveyed objects. Engineered Plastic Top Chains are divided into several types as follows:

(1) Standard series.

(2) Low-friction, wear-resistant series. In the low-friction series, the coefficient of friction (against guide rails or conveyed objects) is 15 to 45 percent lower, and wear life is 1.2 to 2 times longer than standard series.

(3) Heat-resistant, high-speed series. When constructed of super engineered plastic, this series can work continuously in temperatures up to 250°C, and the chains can convey objects with speeds up to 200 m/min.

(4) Anti-chemical series. These chains are made of super engineered plastic and resist most organic solvents, inorganic salts, acids, alkalines, and oxidizers. There is a "super anti-chemical" series with pins made of titanium.

(5) Electroconductive series. This series has electric resistivity of $10^6 \Omega \bullet$ cm. These chains are suitable where dust collection, electronoise, and electrosparks should be avoided.

(6) Plastic pin series. In this series, chains and pins are made of engineered plastic. Compared to the standard series, these chains are 15 to 25 percent lighter in weight and are easy to disassemble for recycling. A larger-diameter pin and unique design make this a very strong series. In fact, it has almost the same allowable tension as the standard series.

Table 4.1 shows the features of each type of TPU 836 chain. Coefficient of friction and maximum allowable load are under the following conditions: room temperature, non-lubricated, chain speed 10 m/min., and stainless steel rail.

4.1.2 Guide Rail Materials

The guide rails for engineered plastic chains are usually made of 304 stainless steel with a good finish, MC nylon, or ultra-high molecular-weight polyethylene (UHMW). For steel chains, guide rails are made of plastic.

For heat-resistant and high-speed applications, make sure you consider the following points:

(1) When the chain operates within normal temperatures at high speeds, choose a guide rail that is made of carbon steel or stainless steel with polished, hard chrome-plating.

(2) When the chain operates in high temperatures, consider a polished stainless steel guide rail. Remember to allow for heat expansion, and fix only one end of the guide rail.

Table 4.1 Types of Engineered Top Chains

	Material	Maximum Chain Speed (m/min.)	Maximum Ambient Temp. (°C)	Coefficient of Friction	Maximum Allowable Load (kN)
Standard	Polyacetal	50	80	0.25	0.98
Low-Friction	Special Polyacetal	50	80	0.17	0.98
Heat-Resistant	Super Engineered Plastic	200	250	0.20	0.98
Anti-Chemical	Super Engineered Plastic	40	80	0.30	0.50
Electroconductive	Special Polyacetal	50	80	0.25	0.70
Plastic Pin	Special Polyacetal	50	80	0.17	0.88

4.1.3 Lubrication

Soapy water used to be applied as a lubricant in food industries, but now a water-based lubricant is more frequently utilized. For general applications that allow oil, use oil to lubricate Top Plate Chains.

4.1.4 Various Accessories

In addition to the chains and sprockets explained in this book, there are a variety of accessories, including guide rails, chain guides, and feet (Figure 4.3).

Figure 4.3   Chain Accessories

4.2 TYPES OF TOP CHAIN

4.2.1 TTP Top Chain

Top Chain: Engineered plastic for linear performance

Application Example

Bottling and canning

TTP Top Chains are used in linear conveyors to transport or accumulate materials that could be easily scratched, such as bottles or cans. Set-ups may use one or more strands of chain.

Construction and Features

(1) In TTP Top Chain, individual top plates made of molded polyacetal are connected using 304 stainless steel pins (Figure 4.4). Due to its simple construction, the chain can be easily washed and cleaned. The basic information is shown in Table 4.2.

(2) Table 4.3 shows the dimensions and function availability for selected TTP Top Chains. In addition to the ones shown in the table, TTP Top Chains are produced in the following widths: 63.5, 76.2, 101.6, 114.3, 127.0, 152.4, and 165.1 mm. Check with the manufacturer about the types of chains available.

(3) Double-hinged TTP Top Chains have wider hinges than standard chains, and are available in Top widths of 190.5, 254, and 304.8 mm. Use 25-tooth sprockets (12.5 effective teeth) for these chains.

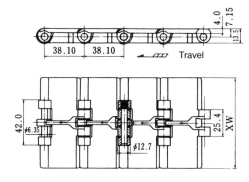

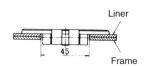

Figure 4.4   TTP Top Chain

Table 4.2 Profile of TTP Top Chain

Chain Pitch (mm)	Bushing Diameter (mm)	Maximum Allowable Load (kN)	Sprocket				Outer Diameter of Idler Wheel
			Number of Teeth	P.C.D.	Steel	Plastic	
38.1	12.7	0.83	9.5	117.33	○	N/A	
			10.5	129.26	○	○	130
			11.5	141.22	○	○	142.5
			12.5	153.20	○	○	154.5 (Segmented)

Table 4.3 Top Plate Dimensions

Top Plate Width (mm)	Standard	Low-Friction	Heat-Resistant	Anti-Chemical	Electroconductive	Plastic Pin
82.6	○	○	N/A	○	○	○
114.3	○	○	N/A	Consult Manufacturer	○	○
190.1	○	○	N/A	Consult Manufacturer	○	○

○: Available

Sprockets

Use special sprockets for TTP Top Chain. Chains may slide off the steel sprocket due to uneven load distribution or misalignment. There are optional guide rings for steel sprockets to prevent this. Engineered plastic sprockets have integral guides at every tooth, or every second tooth.

An engineered plastic idler pulley may be substituted for the sprocket at the tail shaft. The idler pulley rotates freely, without bearings, on the fixed steel shaft.

NOTE: Excessive chain tension can damage the idler pulley.

4.2.2 TP Top Chain

Top Chain: Engineered plastic for linear conveyance

Application Example

TP Top Chains are used for linear conveying. Applications are similar to the TTP series (Figure 4.5).

Construction and Features

(1) There are two specifications of TP Top Chain: Type I and Type II. If you are developing a new application, consider Type II Chain (Figure 4.5). It offers higher wear resistance than Type I.

(2) Tables 4.4 and 4.5 show the main characteristics and available top-plate widths for different chain series.

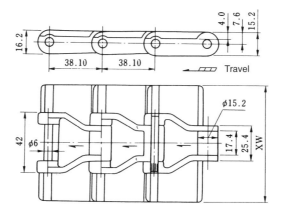

Figure 4.5   TP Top Chain (Type II)

Table 4.4 TP Top Chain and Sprockets

Chain Pitch (mm)	Bushing Diameter (mm)	Maximum Allowable Load (kN)	Sprocket			
			Number of Teeth	P.C.D.	Steel	Plastic
38.1	12.7 (Type I) 15.2 (Type II)	1.18¹	10	123.29	○	N/A
			10.5	129.26	○	○
			11	135.23	○	N/A
			12	147.21	○	○
			13	159.20	○	N/A

¹Refer to manufacturer's catalog for Heat-Resistant series data.

Table 4.5 TP Top Chain Special Feature Availability

Top Plate Width (mm)	Standard	Low-Friction	Heat-Resistant	Anti-Chemical	Plastic Pin
76.2	○	○	N/A	○	N/A
82.6	○	○	N/A / ○	○	N/A / ○
101.6	N/A / ○	N/A / ○	N/A	N/A / Consult Manufacturer	N/A
114.3	N/A / ○	N/A / ○	N/A	N/A / Consult Manufacturer	N/A
127.0	N/A / ○	N/A / ○	N/A	N/A / Consult Manufacturer	N/A

Note: Two symbols in one cell stand for Type I / Type II.   ○: Available

Sprockets

For TP Type II Top Chains, use sprockets for TTU type. Twelve-tooth split sprockets made of engineered plastic (P.D. 147.21) are also available.

An engineered plastic idler pulley may be substituted for the sprocket at the tail shaft. The idler pulley rotates freely, without bearings, on the fixed steel shaft.

NOTE: Excessive chain tension can damage the idler pulley.

When operating in high temperatures, use steel sprockets. If the temperature is higher than 150°C, contact the manufacturer.

Chains for Special Applications

RS2040P chain series, with a top plate width of 50 mm, has a pitch of 25.4 mm. This is smaller than standard Top Plate Chain, which has a pitch of 38.1 mm. With RS2040P, you can use smaller sprockets with 19 teeth (9.5 effective teeth, P.D. 78.23) and select a base material that meets the specific operating conditions, for example, electroconductive, chemical-resistant, super chemical-resistant, or heat-resistant.

4.2.3 TTUP Top Chain

Top Chain: Engineered plastic for curved conveyance

Application Example

Bottling, canning, and general uses

One or more strands of TTUP Top Chains are used for conveying or accumulating objects that are easily scratched, for example, bottles, cans, and finely machined parts.

Construction and Features

(1) TTUP Top Chain is based on engineered plastic TP Top Chain, Type II, but it has extra side-flexing capability. It can curve around corners with minimum radius (R) of 600 mm. This is accomplished with tapered knuckles.

(2) There are no float-prevention tabs on links of TTUP Top Chain (Figure 4.6).

(3) Tables 4.6 and 4.7 show the main functions and available top plate widths for different chain series.

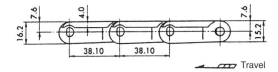

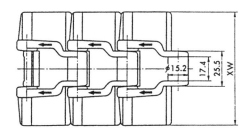

Figure 4.6   TTUP Top Chain

Table 4.6 TTUP Top Chain and Sprockets

Chain Pitch (mm)	Bushing Diameter (mm)	Maximum Allowable Load (kN)	Number of Teeth	P.C.D.	Steel	Plastic	Outer Diameter of Plastic Idler Wheel
38.1	15.2	1.08	10	123.29	○	N/A	N/A
			10.5	129.26	○	○	130
			11	135.23	○	N/A	142.5
			12	147.21	○	○	154.5 (Split is available)
			13	159.20	○	N/A	N/A

Table 4.7 TTUP Top Chain Special Feature Availability

Top Plate Width (mm)	Standard	Low-Friction	Heat-Resistant	Anti-Chemical	Electroconductive	Plastic Pin
82.6	○	○	N/A	○	○	○
114.3	○	○	N/A	Consult Manufacturer	○	N/A / N/A
190.1	○	○	N/A	Consult Manufacturer	○	N/A

○: Available

Sprockets

An engineered plastic idler pulley may be substituted for the sprocket at the tail shaft. The idler pulley rotates freely, without bearings, on the fixed steel shaft.

NOTE: Excessive chain tension can damage the idler pulley.

Selection and Handling

The main difference between TTUP and TPU Top Chain is that TTUP does not have float-prevention tabs. Therefore, TTUP may be more easily detached from guide rails.

4.2.4 TPU Top Chain

Engineered Plastic Top Chain for curved conveyance

Application Example

Bottling, canning, and general uses
TPU Top Chain (Figure 4.7) is used in similar applications as TTUP Top Chain.

Construction and Features

(1) TPU Top Chain has side-flexing capability with a minimum radius (R) of 500 mm accomplished by taper-shaped knuckles, and is equipped with float-prevention tabs on plates. A smaller minimum radius of TPU than on TTUP, and the presence of float-prevention tabs, enables this chain to follow complicated layouts.

(2) Tables 4.8 and 4.9 show the main functions and available widths for various TPU Top Chains.

Figure 4.7   TPU Top Chain

Table 4.8 TPU Top Chain and Sprockets

Chain Pitch (mm)	Bushing Diameter (mm)	Maximum Allowable Load (kN)	Sprocket				Outer Diameter of Plastic Idler Wheel
			Number of Teeth	P.C.D.	Steel	Plastic	
38.1	15.2	0.98	10	123.29	○	N/A	N/A
			10.5	129.26	○	○	N/A
			11	135.23	○	N/A	N/A
			12	147.21	○	○	N/A
			13	159.20	○	N/A	N/A

○: Available

Sprockets

An engineered plastic idler pulley may be substituted for the sprocket at the tail shaft. The idler pulley rotates freely, without bearings, on the fixed steel shaft.

NOTE: Excessive chain tension can damage the idler pulley.

In high temperatures, use steel sprockets. If the operating temperature exceeds 150°C, contact the manufacturer.

Table 4.9 TPU Top Chain Special Feature Availability

Top Plate Width (mm)	Standard	Low-Friction	Heat-Resistant	Anti-Chemical	Electroconductive	Plastic Pin
82.6	○	○	○	○	○	○

○: Available

Selection and Handling

TPU is similar to TTUP except for the following points:
(1) TPU Top Chain has float-prevention tabs.
(2) It is difficult to detach the chain from guide rails.
(3) Float-prevention tabs allow the chain to easily follow any changes in rail direction, from horizontal to vertical (Figure 4.8).

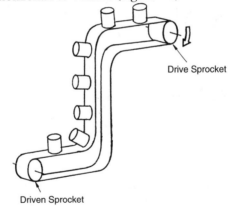

Drive Sprocket

Driven Sprocket

Figure 4.8 TPU Float-Prevention Tabs Allow the Chain to Follow the Direction of the System

4.2.5 TT Top Chain

Steel Top Chain: For linear conveyance, including bottling, paper containers, general uses

Application Example

TT Top Chain is used for linear conveyance of beer and cosmetic bottles, paper containers, or general products.

Construction and Features

(1) TT Top Chain consists of stainless steel top plates with rolled hinges and connecting pins. Due to its simple construction, the chain is easy to clean, and it meets the requirements of sanitary environments. (Figure 4.9).

(2) There are two standard types of TT Top Chain: N-type has 304 stainless steel pins and 430 stainless steel plates; SS-type is made entirely of 304 stainless steel.

(3) Table 4.10 shows the main functions of this chain.

(4) There are eight widths of top plates: 63.5, 76.2, 82.6, 101.6, 114.3, 127.0, 152.4, and 190.5 mm. The top plates have beveled (or chamfered) edges, which permit smooth loading or accumulating of conveyed objects, such as bottles.

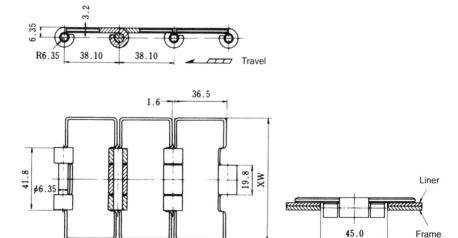

Figure 4.9 TT Top Chain

Sprockets

Use special sprockets for this chain.

If you use steel sprockets, make sure to install guide rings to prevent the chain from sliding off. This can happen if materials are unevenly distributed on the chain, or if the chain is misaligned.

Split engineered plastic sprockets come with guides on every tooth or every other tooth. Therefore, guide rings are not necessary. Maintenance on split sprockets is quite simple. They are easy to install and remove from the shaft.

An engineered plastic idler pulley may be substituted for the sprocket at the tail shaft. The idler pulley rotates freely, without bearings, on the fixed steel shaft.

NOTE: Excessive chain tension can damage the idler pulley.

Table 4.10 TT Top Chain Characteristics

Chain Pitch (mm)	Bushing Diameter (mm)	Maximum Allowable Load (kN)	Sprocket				Outer Diameter of Plastic Idler Wheel
			Number of Teeth	P.C.D.	Steel	Plastic	
38.1	12.7	1.47 (N-type) 2.16 (SS-type)	10.5	129.26	○	○	130
			11.5	141.22	○	○	142.5
			12.5	153.20	○	○	154.5 (Split is available)

○: Available

Chains for Special Applications

Special finishes on the upper part of the plate are available. The ground type has a fine finish to allow for extra-smooth sliding of conveyed bottles. The anti-abrasion finish has hard chrome plating on the upper side of the top plate.

4.2.6 TS Top Chain

Steel Top Chain: For linear conveyance. General uses

Application Example

TS Top Chain is used for linear conveyance. TS-P type allows on-loading and unloading objects along direction of chain movement, when a single strand of chain is used. When objects are conveyed or moved across several strands of chains, TS-PA type works effectively. (Figure 4.10 shows TS-P type.)

Construction and Features

(1) In TS Top Chain, top plates are projection-welded onto RS Double Pitch Roller Chain (RS2060-S).
(2) Table 4.11 shows the main functions of the chain.

Chains for Special Applications

(1) Nickel-plated and 304 stainless steel are available.
(2) The lubrication-free LAMBDA® series (NP-P-LAMBDA, NP-PA-LAMBDA) offers extended chain wear life without additional lubrication (not suitable for wet or dusty conditions).

Figure 4.10 TS Top Chain (P-Type)

Table 4.11 TS Top Chain and Sprockets

Chain Pitch (mm)	Roller Diameter (mm)	Maximum Allowable Load (kN)	Sprocket			
			Number of Teeth	P.C.D.	Steel	Plastic
38.1	11.91	2.94 (P, NP-type) 1.03 (SS-type)	9.5	117.34	○	○
			10.5	129.26	○	○
			11.5	141.22	○	○
			12.5	153.20	○	○

○: Available

4.2.7 TTU Top Chain

Steel Top Chain: For curved conveyance. Bottles, paper containers, or general materials

Application Example

TTU Top Chain is used for curved conveyance of beer bottles, cosmetic bottles, paper containers, or general materials (Figure 4.11).

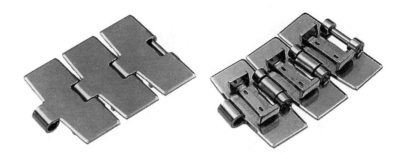

Figure 4.11   TTU Top Chain

Construction and Features

(1) To accomplish curved movement, TTU Top Chain has oval-shaped hinges and float-prevention tabs for curved guide rails. These two features differentiate TTU chain from the TT series.

(2) Table 4.12 shows the main characteristics of TTU Top Chain.

(3) There are four widths of top plates: 63.5, 82.6, 114.3, and 190.5 mm.

Table 4.12 Characteristics of TTU Top Plate Chain

Chain Pitch (mm)	Bushing Diameter (mm)	Maximum Allowable Load (kN)	Sprocket				Outer Diameter of Plastic Idler Wheel
			Number of Teeth	P.C.D.	Steel	Plastic	
38.1	12.7	2.16	10.5	129.26	○	○	130
			11.5	141.22	○	○	142.5
			12.5	153.20	○	○	154.5 (Split is available)

○: Available

4.2.8 TO Crescent Top Plate Chain

Steel Top Chain: For curved movement

Application Example

TO Crescent Top Plate Chain is available for general uses.

Figure 4.12 TO Crescent Top Plate Chain

Construction and Features

(1) Based on RS80 Roller Chain, TO Top Plate Chain is triple pitch (76.2 mm). It can follow any horizontal direction because the top plates installed on each chain link are crescent shaped (Figure 4.12).

(2) You can connect or disconnect this chain at each chain link.

(3) There are three widths of top plates: 82.6, 114.3, and 117.8 mm.

(4) Standard (S) or large (R) rollers are available.

(5) Standard type has carbon steel base chain and top plates made of 430 stainless steel. The SS-type is entirely made of 304 stainless steel.

(6) When the chain is used horizontally, pay special attention to prevent the chain from hanging down. Support top plates with a top plate guide near the sprocket. Use guide rails in other sections of the conveyor.

Sprockets

Use special sprockets. For TOS Chain (S-rollers), use 31 teeth (effective teeth: 10 1/3, P.D. 254.59 mm), for TOR Chain (R-rollers), use 11 teeth (P.D. 270.47 mm).

Selection and Handling

(1) Guiding at the curve: With R-rollers, you can guide the chain with sprockets or guide rails. With S-rollers, you can guide with sprockets, but not with guide rails.

(2) TO Chain is available with nickel plating or all 304 stainless steel. Contact the manufacturer for information.

Chains for Special Applications

(1) TO Top Chains with engineered plastic top plates, plates with bushings, and rollers are available for low-noise, light-weight applications (width: 114.3 mm). Check with the manufacturer.

(2) TU series is designed to operate in any of three directions. (See Figure 4.13.)

Figure 4.13　TU Crescent Top Chain Can Operate in Three Directions

4.2.9 TN Snap-On Top Plate Chain

Top Chain: Engineered plastic top plates. Linear conveyance, general uses

Application Example

TN Snap-On Top Plate Chain is used for conveying and accumulating objects that are easily scratched (Figures 4.14 and 4.15), and can be used alone or several strands in parallel.

Construction and Features

(1) This linear conveyance chain consists of engineered plastic top plates snapped onto outer links of RS60 Roller Chain (chain pitch: 19.05 mm, with nonriveted pin ends). It is easy to install or exchange top plates in this chain. When snap-on top plates of two or more separate chains are guided by the liners, it is possible to move conveyed objects across chains.

(2) Table 4.13 shows the maximum allowable tension and available widths of top plates for base chains made of different materials. Notice the higher maximum allowable loads for carbon steel and plated carbon steel chains.

TN826PC

RS60 Special Base Chain

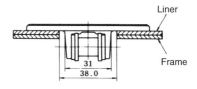

Liner

Frame

31
38.0

Figure 4.14 TN Top Chain

Figure 4.15 TN Top Chain Has Level Top Plates

Table 4.13 Maximum Allowable Loads for Top Plate Chains

Chain Spec.	Maximum Allowable Load (kN)	Top Plate Width				
		82.6	101.6	114.3	127	190.5
Carbon Steel	6.28	○	○	○	○	○
NP	6.28	○	○	○	○	○
SS	1.03	○	○	○	○	○
Poly-Steel	0.88	○	N/A	N/A	N/A	N/A

○: Available

Sprockets

Usually, standard sprockets for RS60 Roller Chain with 19 teeth (P.D. 115.74 mm) through 25 teeth (P.D. 151.99 mm) are used with this chain. Stainless steel and engineered plastic sprockets are also available.

Selection and Handling

(1) Snap-on top plates will not separate from the base chain under normal use. Excessive loads may cause snap-on top plates to separate.
(2) An idler pulley should not be used for this chain.
(3) The back portion of the top plate rises slightly above the level of the conveying surface in the area where the chain engages with the sprocket. This should be considered when designing a system.

Chains for Special Applications

(1) Lube-free LAMBDA® carbon steel or plated chains can be used for clean applications. These chains are most effective if they are not exposed to water, liquid, or dust.
(2) MW top plates are low-friction and abrasion resistant.
(3) TNU Snap-On Top Plate Chain series are used in curved movement.

4.2.10 RS Plastic Top Chain

Top Chain: Engineered plastic. General uses, food industries

Application Example

RS Plastic Top Chain is used in electric, electronic, food (such as bakeries), and other industries (Figure 4.16).

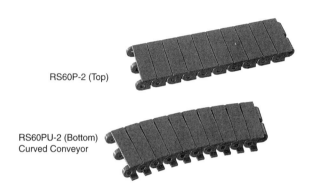

RS60P-2 (Top)

RS60PU-2 (Bottom)
Curved Conveyor

Figure 4.16 RS Plastic Top Chain

Construction and Features

(1) Due to the small chain pitch, the transition area between conveyors is minimal. This ensures smooth loading.
(2) Double strand chain can be used in long conveyors due to increased allowable load.
(3) Table 4.14 shows chain sizes, availability, functions, and specifications.

Sprockets

Standard sprockets will not work with double strand chains, RS60P-2 and RS60PU-2 chain. Special sprockets must be used.

Table 4.14 RS Plastic Top Chain

Chain Number	Pitch (mm)	Top Plate Width (mm)	Maximum Allowable Load (kN)	Standard	Low-Friction	Heat-Resistant*	Anti-Chemical	Plastic Electroconductive	Pin
RS40P	12.70	20	0.44	○	○	○	○	○	N/A
RS60P	19.05	30	0.88	○	○	○	○	○	N/A
RS60P-2	19.05	60	1.27	○	○	N/A	N/A	N/A	N/A
RS60PU-2	19.05	60	1.08	○	○	N/A	N/A	N/A	N/A

* Up to 140° C.   ○: Available

4.2.11 Bel-Top Chain

Top Chain: Engineered plastic belt-shaped chain. Bottling, canning, and general uses

Application Example

Bel-Top Chain offers the power and reliability of a chain system with the smooth operation of a belt. The chain is used for linear conveyance, accumulation, side loading, and movement of cans, bottles, or other materials that are easily scratched (Figure 4.17).

Accumulation and movement with Bel-Top Chain is smoother than a system with several strands of Engineered Plastic Top Chains. In addition, the Bel-Top Chain system, including guide rails and other parts, costs less.

Construction and Features

(1) The chain consists of engineered plastic modular links with small pitch (19.05 mm) and pins. It combines the functions of a chain and belt (Figure 4.18).

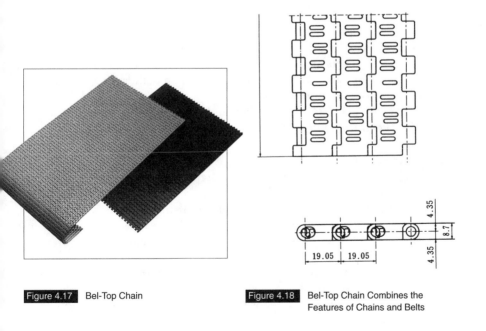

| Figure 4.17 | Bel-Top Chain |

| Figure 4.18 | Bel-Top Chain Combines the Features of Chains and Belts |

(2) There are two types of Bel-Top Chain; MWB type has low-friction and anti-abrasion, KV-type has heat resistance (endures continuous temperatures of up to 250°C) and high-speed resistance. Each type uses different engineered plastic.

(3) Pins are made of engineered plastic in MWB-type and stainless steel in KV-type. There are specially shaped snap rings installed on both ends of the pin to prevent it from falling out.

Special features include the following:

(1) Large conveying width (up to 3 m).

(2) No slippage due to positive engagement with sprockets.

(3) Easy to maintain. The chain consists of only three parts; therefore, it is easy to assemble, connect, and disconnect. If a single link breaks, only the broken parts need to be replaced.

(4) Considering small chain pitch, small sprockets may be used to ensure smooth transfer between conveyors.

(5) Sprockets prevent tracking problems. This condition is difficult to prevent when using a conventional belt.

(6) It is easy to maintain a clean and sanitary operation. Therefore, the chain is widely used in the food industry.

Sprockets

Use special engineered plastic sprockets with 10 teeth (P.D. 61.65 mm) for a hexagonal steel shaft, or 24 teeth (P.D. 145.95 mm) with a square steel shaft. When 10-tooth sprockets are used, the area between conveyors can be minimized. On the other hand, 24-tooth sprockets offer smoother engagement with the chain, and chordal action is reduced.

When conveying light products, the lateral distance between sprockets may be extended. Refer to the manufacturer's catalog for details.

Selection and Handling

(1) Maximum allowable load of both MWB-type and KV-type is 1.96 kN for 1,524-mm-wide chain. However, this value is affected by temperature and speed. When the chain width is greater than 1,524 mm, check the manufacturer's catalog for maximum allowable load.

(2) "Open type" of MWB-type has holes in the upper panel. These can be used in a variety of applications. For example, you can drain liquid or allow air flow through the chain during the operation.

(3) It is important to allow for catenary, and to install take-up on the return side. Special consideration needs to be given to the heat expansion of KV-type.

5. FREE FLOW CHAINS

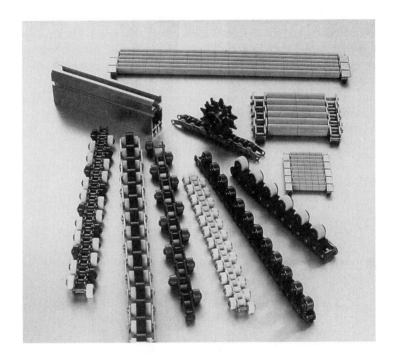

Figure 5.1   Free Flow Conveyor Chains

5.1 WHAT IS FREE FLOW CHAIN?

A free flow conveyor system allows you to stop conveyed objects (with a stopper), while the chain (Figure 5.1) runs continuously underneath. After the stopper is released, conveying resumes (Figure 5.2).

It is possible to get free flow function even with standard RS (figure-eight side plates) roller chains by placing conveyed objects directly on the chains. However, during the accumulating mode, the chain will slide underneath, which may leave marks on the bottom of conveyed objects, and eventually leading to excessive wear.

Free flow chains were developed to eliminate the possibility of damaging conveyed objects during the accumulating mode. These chains are equipped with rollers that support conveyed objects. When accumulating, freely rotating rollers are in contact with the bottom side of goods conveyed, which ensures smooth and damage-free operation.

There are several types of free flow chains. Figure 5.3 shows the relation among various types of free flow chains.

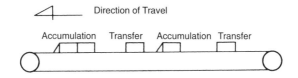

Figure 5.2 Free Flow Conveyor System

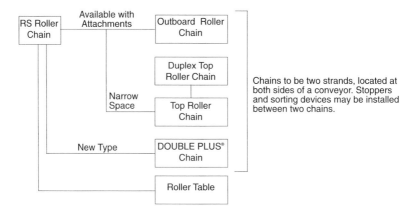

Figure 5.3 Types of Free Flow Chains

5.2 TYPES OF FREE FLOW CHAIN

5.2.1 DOUBLE PLUS® Chain

Free flow conveyance: Light conveyance. Electric, electronic industries

Application Example

DOUBLE PLUS Chain is a new type that meets low noise requirements and high safety standards. It was invented in Japan in the 1980s, and it is now being used around the world for electronics assembly lines as well as in the auto parts, beverage, and medical equipment industries.

The chain is widely used in electric or electronic industries on the assembly lines, where objects (for example, VCRs) are conveyed on pallets. Usually two chains are used as a set (Figure 5.4).

Pallets are usually made of aluminum with steel or plastic (polypropylene) liners at the chain-pallet contact point.

The common pallet type is:

Size: 500 mm × 500 mm.

Weight: 20 to 30 kg (including the weight of conveyed objects).

Pallet speed: 10 to 15 m/min.

Construction and Features

DOUBLE PLUS Chain has large center rollers with small rollers on both sides. During conveyance, large center rollers and small rollers rotate at the same rpm. Chain tension, while conveying objects, is relatively low, as it is affected primarily by rolling friction.

Figure 5.4   DOUBLE PLUS® Chain

Due to the difference in diameter between large and small rollers, the pallets move faster than the chains. The speed ratio (K) is calculated by the following formula:

K = 1 + (large roller diameter/small roller diameter).

The value of K is usually between 2.5 and 3.0.

During the accumulating mode, the large rollers that support the pallet rotate in the opposite direction from the small rollers. Due to this relative motion, friction results between the two rollers, and chain tension increases.

After the accumulator stop is released, the friction between large and small rollers will gradually increase the pallet speed, and eventually the pallet will resume full conveying speed (Figure 5.5).

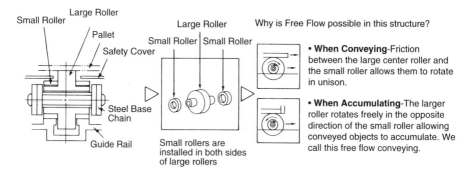

Figure 5.5   Basic Operation of DOUBLE PLUS® Chain

Features of DOUBLE PLUS® Chain include the following:
(1) Safe design, due to only large rollers being exposed when the chain cover is installed.
(2) Low operational noise, due to low chain speed.
(3) High wear resistance, because the large and small rollers are made of engineered plastic.

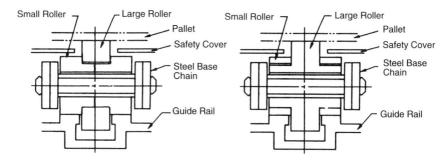

Figure 5.6   Two Types of DOUBLE PLUS® Chain

There are two design types of DOUBLE PLUS® Chain. These are shown in Figure 5.6. In Figure 5.6 (left), the large roller is positioned between two small rollers equipped with a step. The step portions of each small roller face each other and are inserted in the ID of the large rollers, thus holding them in position. In the right-hand illustration, the large roller is equipped with steps on both sides. The small roller is positioned over each step.

Although the designs are different, the performances are practically the same. In Figure 5.6, the left-hand chain has a K speed ratio close to 3, which is slightly higher than the other type.

In the design shown in Figure 5.6 (left) when the chain engages with the sprockets, the large rollers don't lock; therefore, the pallets travel at the normal conveying speed (three times the speed of chain) at the exit or entrance of the conveyor.

In the right-hand illustration, the large rollers lock when the chain engages with the sprockets. Therefore, the pallet speed is reduced to the chain speed at the conveyor exit or entrance. This is convenient if you want to transfer a pallet to another conveyor moving at a slower speed. If sprockets are lowered slightly, constant conveying speed at the exit from the conveyor is maintained.

The sizes of DOUBLE PLUS Chain are shown in Table 5.1.

Table 5.1 DOUBLE PLUS® Chain Sizes

Chain No.	Chain Pitch	Large Roller		Small Roller		Allowable Load kN*
		Diameter	Width	Diameter	Width	
RF2030VRP	19.05	18.3	8.0	11.91	4.0	0.55
RF2040VRP	25.40	24.6	10.3	15.88	5.7	0.88
RF2050RFP	31.75	30.6	13.0	19.05	7.1	1.37
RF2060VRP	38.10	36.0	15.5	22.23	8.5	2.06
RF2080RFP	50.80	48.0	20.0	28.58	15.0	5.29

* Regular Type (A)

Sprockets

Use special 10-tooth sprockets that engage with small rollers (Figure 5.7).

Specialized Sprocket

Figure 5.7   Specialized 10-Tooth Sprocket for Use with DOUBLE PLUS® Chain

Selection and Handling

(1) There are two types of DOUBLE PLUS® base chain: with or without bushings. The bearing area on the type with bushings is larger, creating a contact surface between the pin and bushing. The bearing area on the type without bushings is limited to the contact surface between the side plate and the pin. Chain with bushings has much better wear characteristics.

(2) The guide rail and bottom surface of the pallet should be smooth and straight in a DOUBLE PLUS Chain system for proper operation. Therefore, check and compare that the chain has a flexible construction that can accommodate irregularities.

(3) Large and small rollers are available in different types of materials: standard, electroconductive, and high friction (for increased pallet acceleration). These specifications may be combined to suit your needs.

(4) Aluminum extrusions are usually available through the manufacturer. If the weight on the pallets is very heavy, or you want to extend the working life of the system, steel rails should be used.

(5) If you lubricate between the pins and bushings to reduce the noise and wear elongation, do not allow oil to get on the contacting surface of the large rollers and small rollers or on the outer surface of small rollers. If these parts are contaminated with oil, the pallets will not accelerate fast enough or they won't reach the operating speed because of roller slip. You should buy prelubricated chains.

(6) The rigidity of the chain depends on its structure. The greater the rigidity, the less likely that stick slip will occur (see Basics Section 2.3.5). If the conveyor is less than 15 m long, the possibility of stick slip is greatly reduced.

(7) There will be a gap between head and tail sprockets of two separate DOUBLE PLUS® conveyors when they are positioned in one line. Install a pallet-supporting roller in the transition area (Figure 5.8).

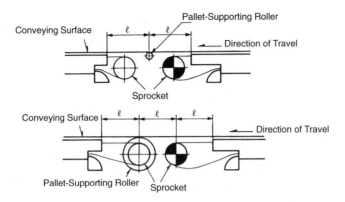

Placement of Pallet-Supporting Rollers

Technical Trends

(1) Small objects, such as screws, may fall between exposed chain components, which can jam the system. Snap covers have been developed to prevent small objects from jamming the line (Figure 5.9).

(2) Besides chain, sprockets, and guide rails, many conveyor components, such as pallet guides (to control side-to-side motion) and brackets, have been designed for DOUBLE PLUS® Chain and guide rails. They are available as kits. Manufacturers are also expected to develop software packages to aid the conveyor designer in selecting the proper chains and components.

(3) There are DOUBLE PLUS® Chains with steel rollers for heavy loads.

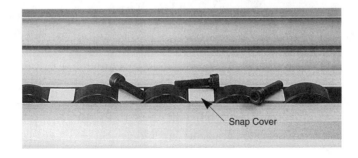

Figure 5.9   Snap Covers on DOUBLE PLUS® Chain

5.2.2 Outboard Roller Chain—Side Roller Type

Free Flow Chain: Electric, electronic and precision machinery conveyance

Application Example

Outboard Roller Chain with Side Rollers (Side Roller Chain) is used for free flow conveyance, like DOUBLE PLUS® Chain, in the electric, electronic equipment, and auto parts industries. Usually two strands are used on the equipment (Figure 5.10). Please refer to DOUBLE PLUS Chain, in Applications Section 5.1.1, for typical pallet size and weight guidelines.

Construction and Features

Side Roller Chain is based on standard roller chain with side rollers installed on extended pins. There are three types of base chain:
(1) RF-type (double pitch roller chain) with S-rollers (straight side plates, small rollers).
(2) RF-type (double pitch roller chain) with R-rollers (straight side plates, oversized rollers).
(3) RS-type (figure-eight side plates, small rollers; oversized rollers are not available).

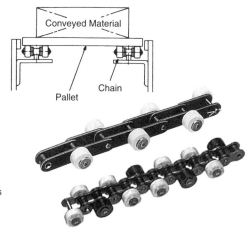

Figure 5.10 Outboard Roller Chain with Side Rollers

You can select various combinations of chain materials; carbon steel, plated carbon steel, various stainless steel materials, and/or engineered plastic. The relation between roller material availability and applicable chain sizes is shown in Table 5.2.

Small sprockets can be used with the RS-type to minimize conveyor height. Because the side roller diameter is larger than the chain pitch for the RS-

Table 5.2 Outboard Roller Chain (Side Roller)

	RS Attachment Type	RF Double Pitch Type
Engineered Plastic Roller	RS40~100	RF2040~RF2100
Electroconductive Plastic Roller	RS40~60	RF2040~RF2060
Steel Roller	RS40~160	RF2040~RF2160

type, side rollers cannot be installed on every pitch on the same side of the chain. They can be installed on every pitch in alternating positions (Figure 5.11).

In RF-type, the diameter and width of the side roller are different for S-rollers and R-rollers.

When the stopper in a free flow conveyor is released, pallets accelerate to the chain speed. This acceleration is determined by the coefficient of friction between the side roller and the pin. The smaller the coefficient of friction, the longer it takes for the pallets to reach the speed of the chain. Faster acceleration can be accomplished by installing brake rollers. The construction and coefficient of friction of the brake rollers are different for each chain manufacturer. In engineered plastic side roller products from Tsubaki, the coefficients of friction of chain are: with brake, 0.10; without brake, about 0.06.

Selection and Handling

Outboard Roller Chain has the following characteristics compared to DOUBLE PLUS® Chain:

(1) Greater allowable tension for the carbon steel chain (Table 5.3).

(2) More economical. RF2050 chain costs about half as much, and sprockets cost about two-thirds that of the equivalent size of DOUBLE PLUS Chain.

(3) More noise. Comparing systems with the same pallet speed and sprockets with the same number of teeth, Side Roller Chain emits about 10 to 15 dB(A) more noise than DOUBLE PLUS Chain.

(4) Because the body of Side Roller Chain is exposed over the guide rail, this chain does not have the same safety features as DOUBLE PLUS.

(5) Snap covers are not available for Side Roller Chain. It is difficult to prevent small objects from falling in between chain components.

(6) Complete kits for Outboard Roller Chain, including the guide rails and other components, are not available. Therefore, you have to create your own system.

Table 5.3 Allowable Tension of DOUBLE PLUS® and Outboard Roller Chains

Chain Type	Roller Type	RF2040	RF2050	RF2060	RF2080
DOUBLE PLUS®	Regular Series	0.88	1.37	2.06	5.29
Chain	High Friction Series	0.44	0.69	1.03	2.65
Outboard Roller	Steel Roller	2.65	4.31	6.27	10.7
Chain	Plastic Roller	0.44	0.69	1.03	1.76

(Allowable load kN)

Sprockets

Standard sprockets may be used. In some cases, side rollers may interfere with the sprocket hub. Additional machining of the hub might be required.

Selection and Handling

(1) Although both R-rollers and S-rollers are commonly used in Side Roller Chains, R-rollers should be considered if either of the following conditions exist:
  • The overall length of the machine is more than 10 m.
  • The chain speed is more than 20 m/min.

(2) R-rollers have lower coefficient of friction (without lubrication, R-roller: 0.12; S-roller: 0.21).

(3) Select Side Roller Chain according to the chain tension and allowable roller load. Make sure to consider the tension due to the accumulating mode when you calculate total chain tension.

(4) Side rollers can be installed in alternating positions, staggered or parallel. Staggered rollers tend to allow pallets to run smoother.

(5) Side Roller Chain requires lubrication to reduce wear elongation and to reduce noise level.

NOTE: Lubrication may affect (delay) acceleration; therefore, please apply carefully.

Chains for Special Applications

Side Roller Chain is available in LAMBDA® construction for lube-free operations.

Technical Trends

Chain manufacturers are working on new chain designs that quiet operation noise.

Chain kits, including chain, guides, sprockets, and other components are a focus of chain manufacturer development plans.

Large pitch side roller conveyor chains are available to handle heavier loads.

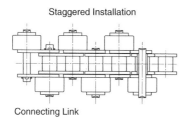

Staggered Installation

Connecting Link

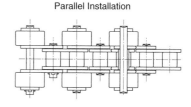

Parallel Installation

Figure 5.11   Installation of Side Rollers

5.2.3 Outboard Roller Chain—Top Roller Type

Free Flow Chain: Automotive industry, precision equipment industry, general uses

Application Example

Outboard Roller Chain with Top Rollers (Top Roller Chain) is used primarily in the automotive and precision equipment industries for free flow conveyance (Figure 5.12).

Construction and Features

Top Roller Chain is based on the standard chain with extended side plates (SK-1 attachments). Top rollers are installed on the pins that connect SK-1 extended plates. Pallets with conveyed objects are loaded on the top rollers. Table 5.4 shows some of the base chains that are available.

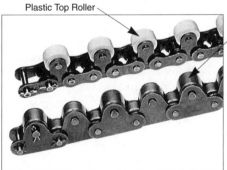

Plastic Top Roller

Steel Top Roller

Regular Series

Figure 5.12   Outboard Roller Chain with Top Rollers

Table 5.4 Outboard Roller Chain (Top Roller)

Base Chain	Top Roller Spacing	Top Roller Material	Chain Pitch	*Max. Allowable Load (kN)
RS Roller Chain	Every Pitch, 2nd Pitch	Steel, Plastic	12.7~31.75	2.65~17.1
Double Pitch Chain	Every Pitch	Steel, Plastic	25.4~63.5	2.65~17.1
Engineering Chain	Every Pitch	Steel	75~200	4.2~35

*Maximum allowable load listed in this table for RS Roller Chain and Double Pitch Chain is the same as that of standard carbon steel chains. For the Engineering Chain, it is one-seventh of the average tensile strength of standard chains.

RS (single pitch) Top Roller Chain can only be equipped with an S-roller. R-rollers and S-rollers are available for RF (double pitch) Top Roller Chain.

The features of Top Roller Chain include the following points:

(1) High maximum allowable tension.

(2) Economical cost.

(3) Lower stability than Side Roller Chain, because Top Roller Chain is narrower.

(4) Snap covers are not available for Top Roller Chain. It is difficult to prevent small objects from falling in between chain components.

(5) Noise levels during operation are higher than those for DOUBLE PLUS® Chain. (Noise is about equal to Side Roller Chain.)

(6) Top Roller Chain installation kits, including the guide rails and other components, are not commonly available.

Sprockets

Standard sprockets can be used with RS (single pitch) chain and with RF (double pitch) chain with S-rollers. Other types of Top Roller Chain require special sprockets.

Selection and Handling

Top Roller Chains are available with R-rollers and with S-rollers. The use of R-rollers is preferred, especially if either of the following conditions exists:

• The overall length of the equipment is more than 10 m.

• The chain speed is more than 20 m/min.

R-rollers have lower coefficient of friction (without lubrication, R-roller: 0.12; S-roller: 0.21).

Chains for Special Applications

Top Roller Chains can be made of stainless steel, carbon steel, or plated carbon steel.

LAMBDA® Top Roller Chain is available for lube-free operations. Engineered plastic top rollers should be used in this construction because they are lube-free.

Two types of Top Roller Chains have higher stability than standard Top Roller Chains (Figure 5.13). They are:

• TG-form with SK attachments that point downward.

• Double Strand Top Roller Chain.

Please refer to Plus α Alpha catalog for additional information.

Double Strand Top Roller	Special Attachment for Prevention of Turnover
TR 	TG 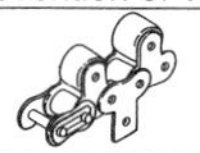

Figure 5.13   Types of Higher Stability Top Roller Chain

5.2.4 Roller Table Chain (ST, RT)

Free flow: Bottling, canning

Application Example

Roller Table Chain lets you convey and accumulate groups of small, separate objects, such as bottles, boxes, or cans. With Roller Table Chain, pallets are usually not used; the conveyed materials are placed directly on engineered plastic rollers. (See Figure 5.14.)

Construction and Features

Roller Table Chain is constructed from two strands of chains, which are connected with stay-pins and engineered plastic rollers that rotate freely. Conveyed objects are placed directly on the engineered plastic rollers. Conveyed goods are accumulated on the Roller Table Chain with low friction.

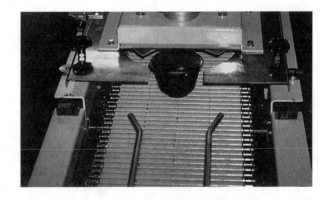

Figure 5.14   Roller Table Chain

There are two types of Roller Table Chain: ST and RT.

(1) ST-type has special attachments that cover the upper side of the chain. These attachments are level with the engineered plastic rollers, which permits low resistance as conveyed objects move across the chain and onto the engineered plastic rollers.

(2) RT-type does not have special attachments that cover the chain. Therefore, side guides are required to prevent smaller conveyed objects from crossing the chain part of the assembly. If the conveyed objects are large (for example, pallets), they can cross the RT-type chain (Figure 5.15).

(3) ST-type is made of 304 stainless steel or nickel-plated carbon steel; RT-type is made of stainless steel.

Features:

(1) The resistance during accumulating (line pressure) is low; the coefficient of rolling friction of engineered plastic roller is 0.06 ~ 0.10.

(2) ST-type is available in pitches ranging from 9.525 to 15.875 mm; RT-type from 9.525 to 19.05 mm. Because the pitch is small, Roller Table Chain is very effective at conveying small objects.

Selection and Handling

Engineered plastic rollers for Roller Table Chain are available in a wide range of effective widths: from 50 to 601.2 mm. Chain width is limited by the conveying capacity, which is usually expressed in kg/m^2.

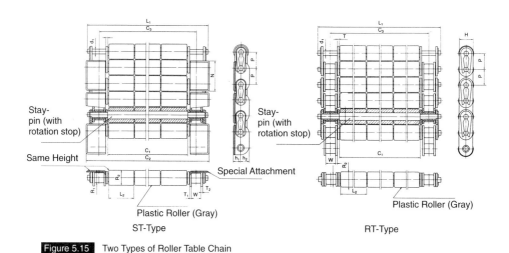

Figure 5.15   Two Types of Roller Table Chain

● Roller Chain Manufacturing Process

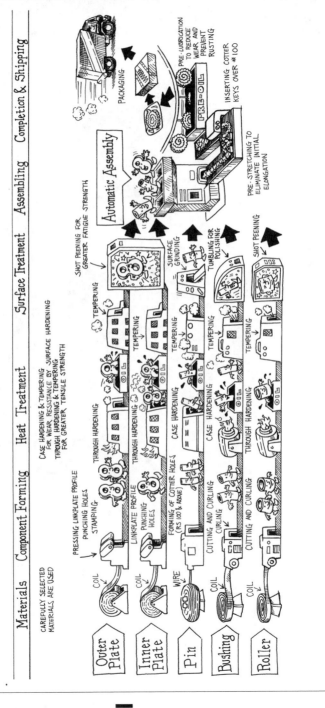

6. LARGE PITCH CONVEYOR CHAINS

Figure 6.1   Large Pitch Conveyor Chain

6.1 WHAT IS LARGE PITCH CONVEYOR CHAIN?

Large pitch conveyor chains (Figure 6.1) are big pitch chains with rollers, originally based on cast iron chains. The base material was changed to steel, and they incorporated some of the features of drive chains and small pitch conveyor chains.

They were standardized by Tsubaki in the 1920s. They were developed in Japan as millimeter-unit pitch chains, available in a variety of pitches for a given capacity. Similar chains are available in the United States, but are usually measured in inch-unit pitch.

6.1.1 Standards

ISO 1977/1 ~ 3 includes standards for large pitch conveyor chains. These standards are for European-type chains, which have larger diameter bushings, pins, and rollers, and thinner, taller side plates than comparable sizes of chains made in the United States or in Japan.

Japan Chain Industry Association Standard JCAS 2-1982 governs seven categories of large pitch conveyor chains. The major characteristics of these categories are shown in Table 6.1.

Table 6.1 Major Characteristics of Large Pitch Conveyor Chain

Chain Number (Pin Dia.)	Tensile Strength (kN)	Pitch (mm)	Side Plate		Inner Link	Roller Diameter	
			Height	Thickness	Width	Small	Large
08	29.4	75~150	23	3.2	15.7	15.9	32
11	68.6	75~150	33	4.7	20.7	22.2	40
14	107.9	100~200	39	6.3	28.7	29.0	50
16	176.5	150~300	46	8.0	35.8	34.9	65
19	205.9	150~300	52	9.5	50.1	40.1	80
22	274.6	200~450	66	9.5	55.9	44.5	100
25	470.7	250~600	81	12.7	65.4	50.8	125

6.1.2 Nomenclature

Some chain manufacturers use their own nomenclature. In the case of Tsubaki, for example, chain size 16 with 200 mm pitch, is listed as RF12200-R. Here's what that name means.

RF 12 200 - R

Average tensile strength, in tons, of the chain when it was originally designed ————

Chain pitch ————

Roller type ————

There are larger sizes than those shown in Table 6.1; in fact, tensile strength can exceed 4,460 kN! If you need extra-high performance chain, discuss the options with the manufacturer.

6.1.3 Construction and Features

The structure of large pitch conveyor chain is shown in Basics Section 1.1.

6.1.3.1 Shape Features

(1) Side plates are straight.

(2) Because the radius of the side plate end is greater than half of the side plate height, the corner of the engaging side plate will rise slightly when the chain joint engages the sprocket. This may cause interference with objects conveyed directly on a chain equipped with an S-roller. (The roller diameter is less than the height of the side plate.)

(3) The end of the pin (opposite to the head of the pin) is equipped with a cotter hole for a T-pin. This arrangement allows easy assembly or disassembly of chain links.

(4) The pin has a swell neck at one end, and the cotter side can either be double flat or have a D-shape. Accordingly, side plates have full round pin holes, and D-shaped or double-flat pin holes.

(5) There are three types of rollers available: R, F, and S (M, N).
The F-roller is a feature of large pitch conveyor chains, since they are useful in guiding the chain on the rail. However, the flange wears against the rail, and therefore, should only be used when the chain is lubricated, or when the conveyed material acts as a lubricant. Additionally, F-rollers should be avoided where heavy loads are conveyed, otherwise the flange may wear quickly or break. As a rule, S-rollers are used to reduce sprocket tooth wear due to smooth engagement with the sprocket, but are not suitable for rolling conveyance.

(6) R- and F-rollers have small-diameter hubs on their sides.

6.1.3.2 Function Features

(1) High rigidity.

Large pitch conveyor chains are designed to carry heavy loads and endure rough loading. Of course, there are limits to the chain's integrity, and it is important to consult the manufacturer for details.

Let us check the chain's resistance to bending. The following formula shows the relationship between bending moment, M, and stress:

$$M = \sigma Z = 1/6 \times \sigma \times H \times t^2$$

σ: stress on side plate
H: side plate height
t: side plate thickness

Using the equation, let's compare the effects of side plate thickness (t) on chain rigidity when tensile strength, side plate height (H), pin diameter, and bushing diameter are held constant.

Here are two examples. Case 1 reflects design considerations for a large pitch conveyor chain; Case 2 is for a small pitch conveyor chain.

Case 1.
Bending moment: $M_1 = 1/6 \times \sigma \times H \times t^2$

Case 2.
$t_2 = t/2$
$\sigma_2 = 2\sigma$ (in order to maintain the same tensile strength)
$M_2 = 1/6 \times \sigma_2 \times H_2 \times (t_2)^2 = 1/6 \times 2\sigma \times H \times (t/2)^2$
Bending moment: $M_2 = 1/12 \times \sigma \times H \times t^2$

Therefore, the large pitch conveyor chain (Case 1) can withstand twice the moment (M) of small pitch conveyor chain (Case 2).

(2) Large pitch conveyor chain is designed to operate in harsh conditions. However, certain environments may affect the side plates, which can lead to stress-corrosion cracking, for example. This is a rare occurrence even for heat-treated side plates of this series.

(3) The chain is designed with relatively large clearances between components. Typically, even if foreign material gets between the chain parts, the rollers will continue rotating, and articulation of the links is not easily impaired.

(4) In Table 6.2, different materials are listed for each chain part of frequently used series. This lets you create a chain specifically for your operating environment at an economical cost. In Table 6.2, the "O" mark designates available materials for the chain parts. Table 6.3 shows the relation of materials and the chain parts.

(5) Attachments have high strength. Take the commonly used A attachment as an example. During operation, it is subjected to bending and twisting forces. Bending moment and twisting moment are calculated according to formulas shown below.

Bending moment (M) = $1/6 \times \sigma \times H \times t^2$
Twisting moment (T) = $A \times \tau \times N \times t^2$

The allowable values of M and T are quite high for large pitch conveyor chain compared with small pitch conveyor chains. Attachments have higher resistance to breakage during operation, but verify the bending and twisting moments. Manufacturers can help you determine the appropriate chain size and attachment for an application.

Table 6.2 Typical Material of Commonly Used Chain Series

	Non-Heat-Treated Steel	Heat-Treated Steel	400 Series Stainless Steel	304 Stainless Steel	Cast Iron
Side Plate	○	○	○	○	✕
Pin	✕	○	○	○	✕
Bushing	✕	○	○	○	✕
Roller	○	○	○	○	○

○: Available   ✕: Not Typically Used

(6) It is relatively easy for users to modify chain attachments, by machining or welding, to fit specific applications. Consult with the chain manufacturer in advance to avoid damaging the chain.

6.1.3.3 Disadvantages

(1) Larger pitch chain increases the size of the equipment, which may be considered an obstacle.
(2) To keep the size of the equipment small when using large pitch chain, sprockets with small numbers of teeth are commonly used. This contributes to greater speed variation of the chain.
(3) Although applications can run as fast as 330 m/min., normally large pitch chains should be used at low speeds.

Large pitch conveyor chains are generally more costly than smaller pitch roller chains, and in the case that the system or the chain does not function as designed, it may be more difficult to resolve these issues than with smaller chains.

You are ultimately responsible for selecting the proper chain, so follow all the steps in the selection process, and consider what effects the system or the conveyed materials have on the chain, in strength, wear, corrosion, etc. As stipulated in previous sections of this book, the calculations of bending and twisting strength of chain attachments, large or small, are the same as with other machine elements.

Work with a chain manufacturer who has a good reputation for quality and safety; who offers knowledge, expertise, and superior service; and who manufactures quality product. Remember, not all chains and attachments are listed in the catalog, as it would be impractical to publish all specifications and information.

Table 6.3 Relationship of Materials and Components

Application			Greater Function	Features
Normal Environment	For Regular	DT	Basic Series	• Most Popular and Economical
	For Wear Resistance	GT	Wear Resistance Between Bushing and Roller	• Greater Wear Life Between Bushing and Roller
		AT	Reinforced Series	• Compact Design • Popular Series
		CT	Wear Resistance Between Pin and Bushing	• Greater Wear Life Between Pin and Bushing • For Cement Conveyor • For Bulk Conveyor
		BT	Reinforced Series	
	For Heavy-Weight Objects	B-DT, B-AT	Bearing Roller Series	• Good For Directly Conveying on the Chain • For Compact Design (Power and Space Saving) • For Unit Conveyor
	For High-Accuracy Positioning	RFN	Bearing Bush Series	• For High Accuracy • Positioning with Indexing Drive on Unit Conveyor
	For Low Noise and No-Lube	DTP	Plastic Roller Series	• Low Noise, Clean, and Light Weight
		RFS-DTP	Plastic Roller and Plastic Sleeve Series	• No-Lube
Corrosive and High-Temperature Environment	For Corrosion Resistance and Heat Resistance	NT	400 Stainless Steel Series	• Corrosion Resistance, Heat Resistance, and Cold Resistance
		PT	Reinforced 400 Stainless Steel Series	
		ST	300 Stainless Steel Series	• Corrosion Resistance, Heat Resistance, and Cold Resistance
Light Corrosive Environment	For Partial Corrosion Resistance	MT	Corrosion and Wear Resistance Between Pin and Bushing	• Incidental Water Contact
		RT	Corrosion and Wear Resistance Between Pin, Bushing, and Roller	• Incidental Water Contact • Good For Conveying Abrasive Bulk Materials
		YT	Reinforced Series	
	For Low Noise and No-Lube	STP	300 Stainless Steel Series Plastic Roller Series	• Clean, Low Noise, Corrosion Resistance • Light Weight
		RFS-STP	300 Stainless Steel Series and Plastic Sleeve Series	• No-Lube

NOTE: 400 Stainless Steel Series Chain May Rust Depending on Environmental Conditions

6.2 STANDARD CONVEYOR CHAINS

6.2.1 RF Conveyor Chain

Large conveyance: Basic type, general uses

Application Example

This is the basic chain series of large pitch conveyor chains (Figure 6.2).

Figure 6.2   Large Pitch Conveyor Chain

Construction and Features

See Basics Section 1.1.

Sprockets

Standard sprockets with 6, 8, 10, and 12 teeth are available for RF Conveyor Chains with R-rollers. For S-rollers, sprockets with 15 and 25 teeth (7.5 and 12.5 effective teeth, respectively) are also available.

The sprockets are sorted into four types according to size, usage, and budget:
(1) Plain bore.
(2) Finished bore with keyway.
(3) Equipped with POWER-LOCK®, a keyless locking device (Figure 6.3).
(4) Detachable tooth.

Figure 6.3　　RF Conveyor Sprocket with POWER-LOCK® Keyless Locking Device

Selection and Handling

Although connecting links are easy to use, the rigidity and strength of the connecting links is less than the other links. If strength is an issue, consider the use of outer links instead of connecting links. Special tools are available to assemble outer links. Check with the manufacturer.

Chains for Special Applications

(1) Bearing-roller series: Lower coefficient of friction and larger allowable roller load.
(2) Plastic roller series: Bushings and rollers are maintenance free.
(3) Plastic sleeve series: Pins and bushings are maintenance free.

6.2.2 RF Bearing Roller Conveyor Chain

Large conveyance: High performance chain. General uses

Application Example

RF Bearing Roller Conveyor Chain is used in automobile, steel, electric, and other industries.

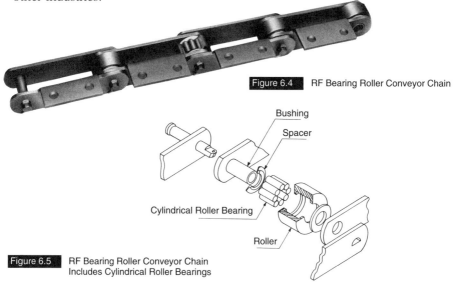

Figure 6.4   RF Bearing Roller Conveyor Chain

Bushing

Spacer

Cylindrical Roller Bearing

Roller

Figure 6.5   RF Bearing Roller Conveyor Chain
Includes Cylindrical Roller Bearings

Construction and Features

In this large conveyor chain, cylindrical roller bearings are installed between the bushing and roller of the RF Conveyor Chain (Figures 6.4 and 6.5).

Compared to basic RF Conveyor Chain, RF Bearing Roller Conveyor Chain has the following features:

(1) The coefficient of rolling friction for RF Bearing Roller Conveyor Chain is one-third to one-sixth that for RF Conveyor Chain.
Basic RF Conveyor Chain: without lubrication, 0.13 to 0.18; with lubrication, 0.08 to 0.12.
RF Bearing Roller Conveyor Chain: 0.03.
This means the chain tension is reduced, and, frequently, a smaller chain size can be used. The conveyor will also require less energy to operate, making it more economical.

(2) The initial cost of equipment is reduced. Because the coefficient of rolling friction is lower, you can use smaller sprockets, motors, reducers, shafts, bearings, and frames.

(3) The allowable load of the roller is increased. The allowable roller load for RF12000-R Bearing Roller Conveyor Chain is 8.35 kN, which is 1.6 to 3.3 times greater than the equivalent size of a basic type with lubrication (2.50 kN for nonheat-treated roller; 4.17 kN for heat-treated roller). Capacity of the roller for RF12000-R Bearing Roller Conveyor Chain is equivalent to RF26200-R Conveyor Chain with heat-treated rollers. This is two sizes larger. In horizontal and slightly inclined conveying, usually the chain size is determined by the allowable load of the roller. Because of the reasons we have discussed, you can select a chain two to three sizes smaller. Rollers are also exposed to high load when they engage with sprockets. Even though this load may be several times greater than the vertical load on rollers during conveying, it is within the capacity range of bearing rollers.

(4) Lower maintenance. RF Bearing Roller Conveyor Chain has grease pockets on both its sides. Although we have received reports that these chains have been operated for five years without any maintenance, we suggest that you lubricate the bearing roller occasionally.

(5) Longevity of the bearing roller. The bearing roller is large in diameter and short in length; therefore, failure due to foreign material getting inside it is rare. Some types of roller bearings are prone to failure due to foreign objects causing misalignment.

(6) Accepting thrust load. A self-lubricating spacer is installed on both sides of the roller to accept thrust load. The spacer prevents a direct contact between the rotating roller and the side plate; therefore, wear particles getting inside the bearing is minimized.

(7) Stick-slip resistance. Stick slip is virtually eliminated because of the low coefficient of friction in a wide range of speeds. Consult the manufacturer when conveyor speed is less than 2 m/min.

(8) Wide range of chain sizes is available. The ball bearings commonly available on the market cannot be adapted for the needs of chains due to their limited load capacity. It is difficult to adapt ball bearings to rollers with diameters less than 45 mm, but roller bearings can be adapted for use by using the bushing and roller as bearing races.

Sprockets

The standard sprockets used for RF Conveyor Chain are used for RF Bearing Roller Conveyor Chain.

Selection and Handling

(1) The design of standard bearing-roller spacers is similar to spacers used in ordinary ball bearings. They are not water- and dust-proof. Oil- or labyrinth-seals can be installed (on a made-to-order basis) if the chain is going to be exposed to water or dust. Please consult the chain manufacturer.

(2) A grease nipple can be installed on the pin head to provide grease to bearing parts (only certain sizes are available).

(3) The working temperature is limited to -20° to 80°C. The limiting factor is the spacer. When a temperature-resistant material is used for the spacer, operating temperatures may be expanded. Contact the manufacturer for additional information.

(4) To reduce the impact of the bearing roller as it engages the sprocket, use sprockets with greater numbers of teeth. For example, if the chain speed is 30 m/min., use a 10-tooth sprocket. Consult with the manufacturer if the chain speed is greater than 30 m/min.

(5) Do not select Bearing Roller Chain based on roller allowable load alone. In some applications, you also need to verify the strength of attachments to prevent breakage. Refer to the manufacturer's catalog for additional information.

Chains for Special Applications

(1) Outboard Bearing Roller Conveyor Chain is used on assembly lines (Figure 6.6). In this type of chain, bearing rollers are installed on the outside of the chain, making it ideal on long assembly lines, like auto lines, where work is performed on the conveyed products along the line. Outboard Bearing Roller Conveyor Chain is easy to support on the return side. If you combine the design features of Outboard Bearing Roller Conveyor Chain and Bearing Bush Chain, you can create a chain with very, very low elongation (practically nonexistent) and minimal rolling friction.

(2) Waterproof-bearing Roller Conveyor Chain (Figure 6.7) has heat-treated bearings made of 403 stainless steel, and includes oil-seals and grease nipples. Originally this chain was developed for the "shower test," which checks the leakage in automobile manufacturing. It can be used in any application where the chain is exposed to water spray.

NOTE: Charge with grease regularly.

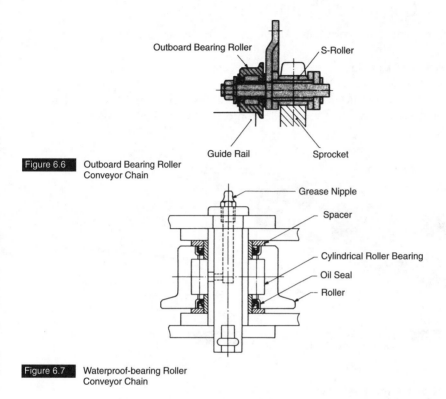

Figure 6.6 Outboard Bearing Roller
Conveyor Chain

Figure 6.7 Waterproof-bearing Roller
Conveyor Chain

(3) Plastic sleeve type. Installation of plastic sleeves between the pins and
bushings makes Bearing Roller Chain maintenance free. It also reduces
the allowable tension. It is available in the following sizes: RF03, RF05,
RF450, and RF10.
(4) A variety of attachments, including special attachments, can be installed
on RF Bearing Roller Conveyor Chain.

Technical Trends

Because of the lower initial cost of the entire installation, RF Bearing Roller
Conveyor Chain has gained acceptance in a wide range of applications. Further
series development is required to respond to various applications.

6.2.3 RF Plastic Roller Plus Plastic Sleeve Conveyor Chain

Large Pitch Conveyor Chain: Maintenance-free type for light load

Application Example

RF Plastic Roller Plus Plastic Sleeve Conveyor Chain is ideal for maintenance-free, light-load applications. It is not suitable for conveying bulk materials (such as grains) or when the application exposes it to rough handling (Figure 6.8).

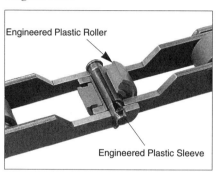

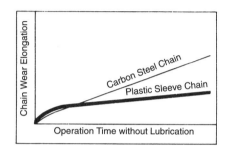

Figure 6.8   RF Plastic Roller Plus Plastic
Sleeve Conveyor Chain

Figure 6.9   Wear Comparison

Construction and Features

See the section on Plastic Sleeve Chain in Small Pitch Conveyor Chains (Figure 6.9).

Sprockets

Standard RF Conveyor Chain sprockets may be used.

Selection and Handling

The maximum allowable load of this chain is smaller than the standard series. For example, maximum allowable load of RF05100-R with plastic sleeve is 5.20 kN (with 8-tooth sprocket), while for the standard type it is 9.80 kN. This represents 47 percent reduction in the maximum allowable load. The coefficient of rolling friction is also 47 percent lower (0.08 versus 0.15 for standard type without lubrication). Therefore, it is important to note that while the maximum allowable chain tension is reduced, the coefficient of friction is also reduced commensurately. The result is that the allowable conveyed object weight on the conveyor remains the same.

6.3 SPECIALTY CONVEYOR CHAINS

6.3.1 Bucket Elevator Chain

Large conveyance: Vertical conveyance of grain and other bulk materials for the cement, chemical, and food industries

Application Example

Bucket Elevator Chains convey bulk materials vertically. You might see this type of chain used to move cement, coal, or grain, for example. Buckets are installed at regular intervals, and the chain moves continuously, scooping and conveying the product. Because they are effective and economical, Bucket Elevator Chains are widely used (Figure 6.10).

When the chain engages the upper sprocket, the buckets are tipped, and conveyed objects are discharged. Discharging occurs either with centrifugal force or continuously, which uses the bottom side of the bucket as a guide for the next bucket.

The trend has been for bucket elevator equipment to become smaller, to economize on installation costs. To reduce the operating costs, the chain must travel faster (more than 80 m/min.). Therefore, the centrifugal discharge bucket elevator has become more common (Figure 6.11). Usually, the capacity of the conveyed material is within the range of 300 ton/h.

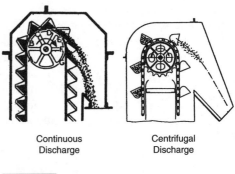

Continuous
Discharge

Centrifugal
Discharge

 Figure 6.10   Bucket Elevator

Figure 6.11   Discharging of Buckets Occurs with Centrifugal Force or Continuously

In large-bucket elevators, two chains are installed, one on each side of the bucket. Small-bucket elevators use only one strand of chain. The two-strand arrangement is a preferable design, ensuring safer operation.

Construction and Features

Bucket Elevator Chain is based on standard large pitch conveyor chain with K-2 or G-4 attachments. Buckets are spaced evenly (usually every two links) over the length of chain.

Three important construction features include the following:

(1) Superior wear resistance of pins and bushings, which reduces chain elongation. This has become increasingly important as cement makers have increased the amount of slag in concrete.
(2) High fatigue resistance.
(3) Easy connecting and disconnecting. This is very important because of the limited space in the elevator housing. Chain must be easy to handle.

Sprockets

Usually, sprockets with 12 teeth are used in low-speed bucket elevators (chain speed less than 45 m/min.). High-speed bucket elevators normally require 24-tooth sprockets. It is important to choose a sprocket with suitable pitch-line clearance.

Excess conveyed material may accumulate in the bottom of the casing, which can cause accelerated wear. Worn chain and sprockets will not engage correctly; the sprockets may have to be replaced. Sometimes, welding material onto the tooth at the point of excessive wear will restore the sprocket, but it is not recommended. Additionally, this procedure is extremely difficult with the sprocket that is located at the top of the bucket elevator.

Even sprockets with hardened teeth are subject to excessive wear in bucket elevators, due to the abrasive nature of conveyed materials. For example, in cement conveyors, there is a point of sprocket hardness at which wear is virtually eliminated. However, it is impractical and expensive to make such hard teeth in standard sprockets. In the 1980s, detachable-tooth sprockets were developed, which permit the replacement of the tooth part only (Figure 6.12). The body of the sprocket remains on the shaft, which reduces repair time and costs. By using special materials in the tooth insert, high tooth hardness is achievable, and therefore, wear life is increased. Use of detachable-tooth sprockets is increasing, especially in the cement industry.

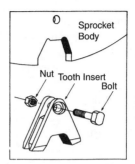

Sprocket Body

Nut Tooth Insert
Bolt

Figure 6.12 Detachable-Tooth Sprocket

Selection and Handling

(1) Choose Bucket Elevator Chain carefully. If the chain breaks, it is extremely difficult and time consuming to remove broken chain from the bottom of the casing. Re-installation is also very demanding. Rely on chain from manufacturers with proven records for quality and reliability.

(2) Use special tools to connect and disconnect chain links.

(3) Avoid grinding the pins, heating the plates, or increasing the size of side plate holes during chain assembly. These procedures, sometimes used at facilities, allow easier assembly of links; however, it compromises the strength of chain, which can lead to ultimate failure.

(4) Consider using detachable-tooth sprockets.

(5) For safety reasons, inspect chain and sprockets frequently, since chains and sprockets have a limited useful life.

6.3.2 Flow Conveyor Chain

Large conveyance: Conveyance of bulk materials in a closed case; cement, chemical, and food industries

Application Example

Flow Conveyor Chain moves bulk materials in a closed case. It conveys the particles horizontally, on a slight incline, or vertically in an arrangement shaped like the letter L. This conveyor is sometimes called a Redler Conveyor (Figure 6.13).

Generally, a flow conveyor is used widely in the conveyance of bulk materials such as cement and fertilizer in chemical industries, and grain in food industries. Because it is enclosed, dust from the conveyed materials is contained, and will not pollute the surrounding area. A flow conveyor is not usually used to move sticky, dusty, or low-density products.

A flow conveyor set up to move cement has an average capacity of 300 ton/h and a speed of 35 m/min. Usually one strand of chain is used.

Figure 6.13   Flow Conveyor Chain

Construction and Features

Specially shaped attachments with large clearances (Figure 6.13) are installed on small pitch or large pitch conveyor chains. The chain operates in a casing filled with conveyed material, such as grain, flour, or ash.

This is based on a phenomenon used in a basic science experiment; when you put sand in a long cylinder, closed at one end with paper, and push the sand with all your strength, the paper cannot be broken if the cylinder is long enough. This is because the friction between the sand and the cylinder absorbs all of the pushing force. Conversely, in the flow conveyor, the attachments work as moving walls, and the sand moves along with it. To lift conveyed objects, the friction at the bottom wall of the conveyor must support the weight of the vertical portion, therefore, the conveyor must have a bottom line "L" shape.

Because there is very little relative movement among the conveyed materials in this application, breakage is rare. The case width is determined by the attachment dimensions; usually it is less than 750 mm.

Chains for flow conveyors include: RF03075 (average tensile strength, 29 kN) through RF26200 (314 kN) for grain conveyance; RF450W (108 kN) through RF36300N (868 kN) for other applications.

Sprockets

Standard sprockets for RF-type conveyor chain are used for flow conveyors. Detachable tooth sprockets are beginning to be used these days.

Selection and Handling

(1) There are several types of attachments available, depending on design and arrangement of the conveyor and whether material is pushed against the bottom of the casing or its side walls.

Figure 6.14 shows several types of attachments (L, B, U₂V, and W). The set-up on the right-hand side has more pushing power than the one on the left-hand side. The specific properties of the material conveyed determine the type of attachments that should be used. Discuss your application with the manufacturer.

| L | B | U_2V | W |

Figure 6.14   Examples of Attachments for Flow Conveyor Chain

(2) KL-type attachment is an inclined version of an L attachment. This attachment can convey low-density and sticky materials.

(3) In grain applications, installation of a cleaner prevents mixing of different types of grains, and the cleaner removes any particles in the casing that could go bad. Usually the cleaner is installed at intervals of 6 m (Figure 6.15).

(4) An M-roller, which rotates more smoothly than an S-roller, is typically used in the base chain.

(5) If the conveyed materials are highly abrasive materials, special block chain provides longer wear life. (Figure 6.16 shows a set-up with NFX-type block chain.)

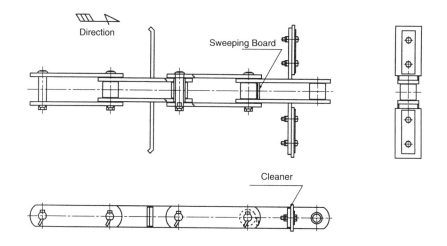

Figure 6.15   Installation of a Cleaner on a Flow Conveyor Chain

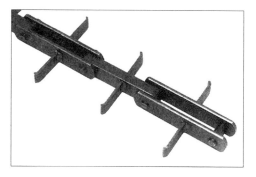

Figure 6.16   NFX-Type Block Chain

Coffee Break

A Brief History of Chain

The word meaning "chain" can be traced back to an ancient word in the Indo-European language family. As early as 225 BC, chain was used to draw a bucket of water up from a well. This very early bucket chain was composed of connected metal rings.

In the 16th century, Leonardo da Vinci made sketches of what appears to be the first steel chain. These chains were probably designed to transmit pulling, not wrapping, power because they consist only of plates and pins and have metal fittings. However, da Vinci's sketch does show a roller bearing.

It took some time for the technology to catch up with the concept. Problems in the manufacturing and processing of steel prevented chain growth until the 19th century, when new technologies made steel chain and bearings realities. In the 1800s, a Frenchman named Gull obtained a patent for a similar chain for use on a bicycle. This chain, called "Gull Chain," is still used today in hanging applications.

When molded chain was invented in the 19th century, things began to move rather quickly. First came the cast detachable chain, which is composed of identical cast links. Next, the pintle chain, which has a separate pin, appeared. The cast detachable chain and the pintle chain have been improved over the years, and they are still in use today in some special applications. They are being replaced—gradually—by large pitch steel conveyor chain.

In the late 1800s, a new development—the bushing—revolutionized steel chain. Chains with bushings had greater wear resistance than Gull Chain because the bushing acted as a bearing, protecting the pin. At this point, the chain story moves into superspeed. Steel bushing chain was used on bicycles, in the rear-wheel drive of early automobiles, and, in 1903, as the propeller drive in the Wright brothers' airplane.

Airplane built by the Wright brothers

First drawing of chain during the Renaissance by Leonardo da Vinci

6.3.3 Parking Tower Chain

Large conveyance

Application Example

Shortage of parking in large cities created a demand for carousel-type (vertical-rotation) multilevel parking, that first appeared in Japan in 1962 (Figure 6.17). Tower parking lots permit the storage of many vehicles (usually more than 30 cars) in a small space. Over the years, tower parking has become increasingly popular. Currently there are more than 10,000 of them in Japan.

Parking Tower Chain supports and rotates the cage containing the vehicle. As an interesting note: Elevator parking garages, which use transmission roller chains or wire ropes to raise and lower the vehicles, are increasing in number. But vertical-rotation garages are still the majority.

Construction and Features

There are only a few manufacturers producing parking tower systems. However, each manufacturer produces a specific design.

Figure 6.18 shows an example of Parking Tower Chain.

The entire assembly consists of chain, attachments, and side rollers. The chain receives tension, which can be summarized as follows:

Chain tension = weight of automobiles and cages + weight of the chain
+ friction on the side roller + tension from take-up.

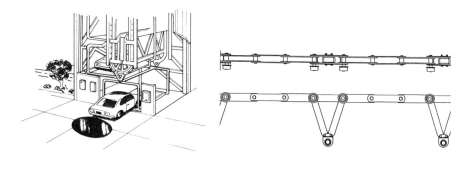

Figure 6.17   Vertical Rotation Parking Elevator   Figure 6.18   Example of Parking Tower Chain

Each attachment must support the weight of an automobile and a cage. The side rollers prevent the attachments from tilting. Spacing of each cage is between 1,600 and 2,000 mm, and attachments are installed on every fourth chain link. Therefore, the chain pitch is 400 to 500 mm. Tensile strength varies between 1,333 and 1,500 kN, depending on the type of chain that is used (the largest one is 2,940 kN). Standard chain speed is 16 m/min., but in some applications speeds reach 25 m/min.

Sprockets

The special shape sprocket with 12 teeth is used with this chain. Usually the sprocket is made by the original equipment manufacturer.

Selection and Handling

(1) Safety is a major concern with this application. The technical standards developed by the Japan Parking Industry Association require a safety factor of more than seven.

(2) It is very important that the original equipment manufacturer (OEM) and the chain manufacturer work closely to select the design and size of the chain for the application. Only manufacturers with experience in this type of application should be considered.

(3) Make sure to include the weight of the chain itself in calculations. It is an important factor, since the number of cars that can be stored may be affected by the weight of the chain.

(4) Pins, bushings, and side rollers must be lubricated regularly, and all components must be inspected frequently. These should be included in the maintenance contract from the OEM.

Technical Trends

Desirable characteristics for Parking Tower Chain include low noise, high-speed stability, light weight, and maintenance free.

6.3.4 Continuous Bucket Unloader Chain

Large conveyance: For conveyance of iron, stone, coal, and rock salt

Application Example

Continuous Bucket Unloader Chain is used to remove large quantities of material, like iron, stone, coal, or rock salt from a ship's cargo hold (Figure 6.19). This application originally used a cable-driven bucket on a crane rather than chains. However, there were several problems with the original design—contamination of the environment by conveyed material, difficulty with automation, inability to scoop material in hard-to-reach areas, and short working life of wire rope. Because of these problems, chain has become the design of choice in current applications.

Figure 6.19   Continuous Bucket Unloader Chain

In this conveyor form, buckets that scoop conveyed objects are installed between two chains. Mobility and flexibility make this equipment different from the conventional bucket elevator. The conveyor system can be moved to different locations, and the equipment can be transformed from an L-shape to an I-shape to get to hard-to-reach areas.

The maximum conveyance capacity: 3,000 ton/h.

The maximum chain speed: about 100 m/min.

Some types of flow conveyors are used for unloaders.

Construction and Features

Chains used in continuous bucket unloaders are exceptionally large, even when compared to other large pitch conveyor chains. Average tensile strengths are 3,040 kN, 3,630 kN, and 4,460 kN for some of the heaviest chains. Usually N-rollers are used in the chain.

Sprockets

The sprockets are exposed to high speeds, heavy shock loads, and corrosive and abrasive materials. Special sprockets with more than 12 teeth and with a noise-reduction factor should be used. Wear-resistant, detachable-tooth sprockets are frequently used.

Selection and Handling

(1) The chain must have exceptional wear resistance because it is exposed to high speeds, heavy shock loads, and conveyed materials that are corrosive and abrasive. For example, in the case of coal, the corrosiveness varies with each coal mine.

(2) Chain attachments should have high strength to support large bucket loads.

(3) Noise and abrasion of sprockets are important considerations.

(4) Choose chain from a manufacturer with a lot of experience and known to produce a high-quality product. Select the chain only after communicating application requirements to the manufacturer.

(5) Assembly of large pitch conveyor chain on the equipment can be an enormous task. There are special tools available that can assist in connecting the chain.

Technical Trends

Manufacturers are working to develop relatively light-weight chain for the load it carries, and sprockets that can provide long-term performance with low noise levels.

6.3.5 Large Bulk Handling Conveyor Chain (CT)

Large conveyance: The steel industry, container conveyance

Application Example

Large Bulk Handling Conveyor Chain (CT) is used in the steel industry to convey hot steel coils (up to 700°C) as well as slabs or other heavy objects, such as containers. This chain is very strong. It can convey several coils, which can weigh up to 45 ton/coil.

Construction and Features

CT Chain is used in pairs, and heavy objects are conveyed directly on them. Standard large pitch chains do not have enough capacity to support the extremely heavy loads (the limiting factor is the roller). For that reason, special cylindrical bearing rollers have been developed. They combine a high allowable load for the roller with low coefficient of friction. The coefficient of friction is 0.03, which is one-third to one-fourth the coefficient of friction of standard large pitch conveyor chain in normal temperatures.

Figure 6.20 and Table 6.4 show the structure, dimensions, and functions of this chain.

A coil can be conveyed on its side or straight up. When the coil is on its side, you can use the chain as shown in Figure 6.20. Special attachments need to be used when conveying a coil straight up. Figure 6.21 shows examples of Large Bulk Handling Conveyor Chains with attachments for conveying round objects, and one for curved conveyance.

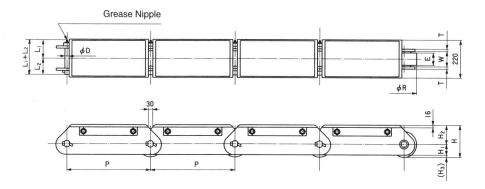

Figure 6.20 Large Bulk Handling Conveyor Chain (CT)

Table 6.4 Dimensions and Functions of Large Bulk Handling Conveyor Chain (CT)

Chain No.	Pitch (mm)				Roller Dia. (R)	Link Plate Height (H)	Max. Allowable Roller Load (kN)	Max Allowable Load (kN)
CT 60	300	400	500		125	171	29.4	83.3
CT 90	300	400	500		135	182.5	35.3	126
CT 130	300	400	500		150	195	42.2	181
CT 160		400	500	600	175	227	55.9	224

Figure 6.21 Large Bulk Handling Conveyor Chain (CT) with Special Attachments

Sprockets

Large Bulk Handling Conveyor Chain requires special sprockets. They must operate at low speeds (less than 15 m/min.) and usually have six to eight teeth, which keeps the diameter small, and cost down.

Technical Trends

The coils are sometimes very hot, and are frequently transported through a heat chamber. For these applications, the chain must be heat-resistant. In one specific case, steel slabs were placed directly on the chain in five piles. Each pile weighed 80 ton, and the surrounding temperature was 900°C. In extreme situations like this, consult the manufacturer.

6.3.6 Block Chain (Bar and Pin)

Large conveyance: The steel industry, conveyance of sand and earth, shuttle traction

Application Example

Block Chain is used for cooling high-temperature steel bars, seamless pipes, or for pushing red-hot slabs and billets, for example (Figure 6.22). In addition to the steel industry, Block Chain is used for vertical conveyance of sand and earth, and for shuttle traction.

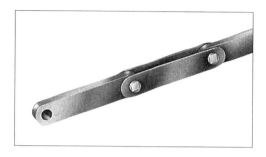

Figure 6.22   Block Chain

Construction and Features

This chain is usually composed of three parts: two outer plates and one (or sometimes two) inner plate (block) that are connected with pins. The tensile strength ranges from 309 to 2,720 kN.

In comparison to roller chain, Block Chain has the following features:
(1) Greater impact resistance due to the strong construction and high rigidity.
(2) Higher strength considering chain weight.
(3) All the main parts are heat-treated for greater wear resistance against the guide rails.
(4) Usually the bottom side of the plate slides on the guide rail; the chain does not have rollers. It's possible to push and carry conveyed objects on the guide rails using special pushers (dogs) attached to the chain (Figure 6.23).

1. Solid Pusher
Inner or outer pusher
link to push material.

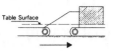

3. Ducking Dog
The dog is supported on
the guide rail to convey
material. When the
guide rail is interrupted,
the dog ducks down,
leaves the material, and
passes beneath it.

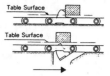

2. Tilting Dog
When material on the
conveyor runs relatively
faster than the chain,
the dog is pushed down
from behind to enable
material to pass over.
The dog then resumes
its original position.

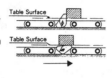

4. Tilting and Ducking Dog
Both tilting and ducking
functions are combined.
When the dog comes in
contact with the table
surface, it lets the material
pass over. When the guide
rail is discontinued, the
dog leaves the material,
and passes beneath it.

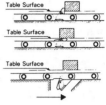

 Figure 6.23   Installation of Pushers
on Block Chain

Sprockets

Sprocket teeth engage the inside plate of the chain, entering the area
between outer links. The sprocket skips every second tooth to allow for the
solid block.

Selection and Handling

(1) Select a sprocket with more than 12 teeth.
(2) Use a sprocket with an outer plate support piece (Figure 6.24).
(3) Install hardened bushings in the inner link for improved wear elongation
resistance (Figure 6.25).

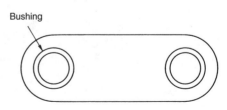

Bushing

Figure 6.24   Sprocket with Outer
Plate Support Piece

Figure 6.25   Hardened Bushings
Improve Wear Resistance

6.3.7 Sewage Treatment Chain (Rectangular Sludge Collector)

Large conveyance: Sewage treatment equipment

Application Example

One of main uses of large pitch conveyor chain is in water treatment facilities. In a large sewage treatment facility, sewage goes through several tanks in which solid wastes are eliminated by deposition and flotation.

In the silt tank, sand and dirt are removed using vacuum or V-buckets. In the settling tank, sludge in the water, or on its surface, is scraped to the exit with "flights" (boards) installed between two strands of chains at intervals of 3 m (Figure 6.26). Sewage Treatment Chain (ACS Chain) is used in this process (Figure 6.27). Accumulated dirt is removed with pumps.

Cast iron chains were once used in sewage treatment facilities. In such a corrosive environment, chain deterioration could not be avoided. As the volume of chain material decreased due to corrosion, wear was accelerated. To offset the loss of material due to corrosion, cast iron chains became quite heavy, yet the tension required in water-treatment applications did not justify the use of a chain with such high tensile strength.

In the mid-1960s, ACS stainless steel chains were developed in Japan especially for water treatment facilities. The stainless steel construction assured excellent corrosion resistance, so there was no need for extra-heavy cast iron chains. Because of their superior functions, ACS chains have gained wide acceptance.

This chain is also used to convey corrosive objects in general scraper conveyors.

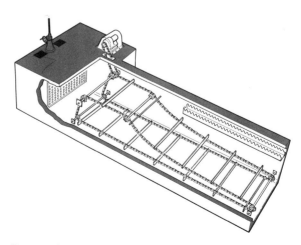

Figure 6.26   Sewage Treatment Chain with Flights Installed

Figure 6.27 Sewage Treatment Chain

Construction and Features

ACS Chain has large-diameter bushings. It does not have rollers.

Plates, pins, and bushings are made of 403 stainless steel. The T-head cotter key is made of 304 stainless steel, which ensures high corrosion resistance.

SF-4 attachments are used for installing flights, and extended pins or LA-1 attachments for installing buckets in the dredger. Both of these attachments are placed on the outer plates. LA-1 attachments are made of heat-treated carbon steel.

Figure 6.28 compares the strength of cast iron chain and stainless steel chain in a long-term test.

Applications

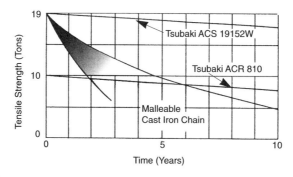

Figure 6.28 Comparison of Cast Iron and Stainless Steel
Sewage Treatment Chain

Sprockets

Use special sprockets. Refer to the manufacturer's catalog.

When cast iron chain was used, cast iron sprockets were also required. Due to corrosion, the area of the sprocket tooth engaging with the chain would lose its original form and round off (Figure 6.29). Upon engagement with the chain, additional stresses would appear that would accelerate wear on the chain and the sprocket even further. As a result, the working life of cast iron chains and sprockets was short.

In an ideal situation, stainless steel sprockets are used with stainless steel chain to ensure the optimum performance. Cast iron sprockets will wear in a similar fashion even if stainless steel chain is used, resulting in increased wear on the chain bushings and shortened chain life. It is a basic point that you must use stainless steel chain and sprockets together. However, stainless steel sprockets are expensive. Chain manufacturers have designed the insert-tooth sprocket to reduce the cost. Only the part of the tooth that engages the chain is stainless steel; the sprocket body is carbon steel (Figure 6.30).

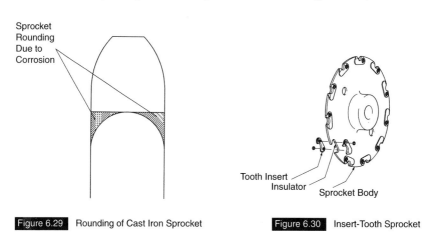

Figure 6.29 Rounding of Cast Iron Sprocket

Figure 6.30 Insert-Tooth Sprocket

Selection and Handling

(1) The chain speed of a scraper application is slow, 0.3 to 0.6 m/min., and 3 m/min. in the bucket application. The chain tension is the highest during the test period, before water is poured into the tank. Before water is poured into a 40-m tank, one chain is exposed to tension of 10 kN.

(2) 403 stainless steel chain has sufficient corrosion resistance for most sewage facilities. If there is a high concentration of chlorine (as found in sea water, for example), if there are high levels of sulfur from hot springs, or if the tanks are contaminated, 304 stainless steel should be used, at least for side plates.

Chains for Special Applications

Chains used in water treatment applications are operated at low speeds and not subjected to any heavy shock loads. It is not necessary in this application to consider chains with tensile strength greater than 19 tonf.

For that reason the following chains were developed:

(1) ACR 810 Chain is a small chain made of 403 stainless steel. It has a tensile strength of 10 tonf. This was the first chain to be used in scraper applications to be equipped with rollers. The rollers reduce wear on the sprocket and the chain. Insert-tooth sprockets have been developed for this chain as well. (See Figure 6.30.)

(2) Engineered plastic chain (ACP Chain, Figure 6.31), developed in the United States, is a light-weight chain with high corrosion resistance. It does not have rollers (similar to cast iron chain). Due to its light weight (one-half to one-fourth the weight of stainless steel chain), installation is relatively simple.

One of the problems with this chain is that engineered plastic expands and contracts as the water temperature changes. Therefore, it is difficult to keep the chain under constant tension. Tensile strength (25 to 40 kN) is much lower than either cast iron or stainless steel chain.

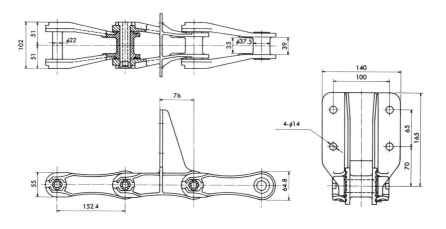

Figure 6.31 Engineered Plastic Chain (ACP Chain)

The material, strength, and dimensions of engineered plastic chains differ from one manufacturer to another. Compare these points when you select the chain.

For engineered plastic chains, there are plastic kits, which include sprockets, flights, and shoes (see Figure 6.32). Use them together. Never use cast iron sprockets with engineered plastic chain.

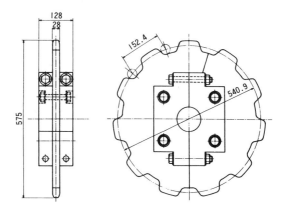

Figure 6.32 Sprocket for Engineered Plastic Chain

6.3.8 Sewage Treatment Chain (Bar Screen)

Large conveyance: Sewage treatment equipment

Application Example

At the water gate of sewage treatment plants, there are gratings—called bar screens—arranged lengthwise to catch floating objects. In addition to water treatment plants, bar screens may be installed at the mouths of rivers. In some bar screen setups, chains are set on guide rails and used as wide gratings or screens. (See Figures 6.33 and 6.34.)

Eventually gratings fill up with contaminants, and they have to be cleaned. A comb-shaped rake installed between two strands of chain is used for this purpose.

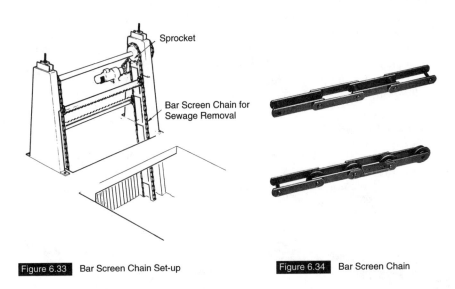

Sprocket

Bar Screen Chain for Sewage Removal

| Figure 6.33 | Bar Screen Chain Set-up

| Figure 6.34 | Bar Screen Chain

Construction and Features

(1) Bar Screen Chain is constructed like roller chain. There are three specifications in this kind of chain. Select the appropriate type based on the corrosiveness of the operating environment (Table 6.5).

(2) Available attachments—Y and A-2 (Type I)—are made of heat-treated steel.

(3) S-rollers and F-rollers may be used with this chain. The difference between the two include the following points:

S-roller: Adapted to a rake with wheels. The rake rotates and sweeps out the waste. (This is sometimes called a rotating-rake design.)

F-roller: Adapted to the rake without wheels. The rake is fixed on the chain. The F-rollers support the weight of the rake. In an F-roller set-up, the flange may alternate sides every one or two rollers. This arrangement prevents derailment. Because the inside width (W) of the chain is larger with the F-roller, the chain is called PJW specification to distinguish it from others (Figure 6.35). Each chain attachment is exposed to high load, because there are only two or three rakes installed on the chain. Y attachments are used in the rotating-rake design (Figure 6.36), and A-2 (Type I) attachments are used in the fixed rake type (Figure 6.37). Both attachments have additional features that increase their strength: the end of the connecting pin is threaded and equipped with a nut to prevent falling off.

Table 6.5 Specifications for Bar Screen Chain

	Side Plate	Pin, Bushing, Roller
Standard Series	Heat-Treated Steel	Heat-Treated 400 Series Stainless Steel
PJ Series	Heat-Treated 400 Series Stainless Steel	Heat-Treated 400 Series Stainless Steel
SJ Series	304 Stainless Steel	304 Stainless Steel

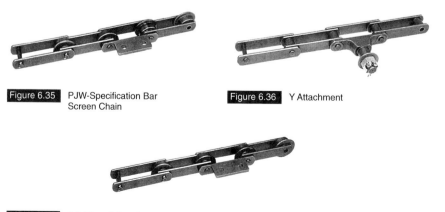

Figure 6.35 PJW-Specification Bar Screen Chain

Figure 6.36 Y Attachment

Figure 6.37 A-2 (Type I) Attachment

(4) F-rollers are exposed to extremely high load from the rakes attached to the chain. To extend the working life, bushings usually have a larger bearing area, which reduces bearing pressure.

(5) Common chain sizes have tensile strength within the range of 68 to 490 kN.

Sprockets

Although these chains are based on RF conveyor chain, they require special sprockets because of the pitch (152.4mm = 6 inches). For S-roller type, insert-tooth sprockets are available.

Selection and Handling

(1) To select this chain, verify the chain tension required, and make sure to confirm the roller load and attachment strength (twisting moment and bending moment).

(2) Allow for a safety factor to withstand peak loads during jam-ups.

(3) Chain rollers might be exposed to high loads when following the curves of the guide rail. Make sure you take this load into consideration when selecting the chain. Minimize tension from the take-up (Figure 6.38).

(4) Of course, you should avoid contaminating the water with oil, but when the test run of the equipment is performed without water, the chain's moving parts should be lubricated.

Corner Rail

Figure 6.38 High Roller Load Due to Curved Rail

Technical Trends

Bar Screen Chain is required to perform with low noise levels, because it is now commonly used near populated areas.

6.4 STANDARD ATTACHMENTS

Large pitch conveyor chains are usually used with attachments. These attachments are divided into the following categories:
- Standard
- Industry-specific (Plus α Alpha)
- Special

Attachment styles and nomenclature for large pitch chains are the same as for small pitch chain. (See Applications Sections 2.3 to 2.5.)

The standard attachments for large pitch conveyor chains are A, K, SA, SK, G, and RFD type. These attachments are available on the following types of chains:
- Treated surface, such as plated chain.
- 304 stainless steel or other special materials.
- Bearing roller or bearing bush specification.

1. A attachment
2. K attachment
3. SA attachment } Refer to Applications Section 2.3 for
4. SK attachment   descriptions of these types of attachments.
5. G attachment

One plate in a pair has bolt holes. These are used to install buckets on two sets of chains (Figure 6.39).

Figure 6.39 G-4 Attachments

6. RFD attachments

The upper side of the link plate is tall; it actually sticks above the R-roller (Figure 6.40). Therefore, conveyed objects can be placed directly on the chain. This is a very economical design.

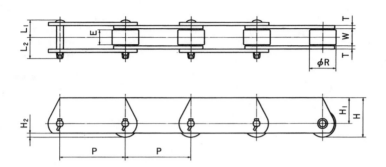

Figure 6.40   RFD Attachments

6.5 PLUS α ALPHA ATTACHMENTS

Although these are not standard attachments, tooling is available. They have been used in a variety of applications, and they have proven to be effective. Please try to incorporate them in your designs.

These attachments are also available with the chains shown below:
- Treated-surface type, such as plated chain.
- 304 stainless steel or other special materials.
- Bearing roller or bearing bush specification.

Tables 6.6, 6.7, and 6.8 show the major types of industry-specific attachments.

Applications

Table 6.6 Plus α Alpha Attachments

Chain Name	Attachment	Appearance	Usage or Application
With CA2	CA2		For a net conveyor that has limited clearance between slats next to each other at sprocket engagement.
With AA3	AA3		To have a reinforced attachment, inserting conveyed jigs into it.
With Reinforced Rib	A2R		To have high flexural rigidity of A attachment.
With MG2	MG2		The same size bucket can be installed.
With AS2	AS2		For installing scrapers or flights.
With AF2	AF2		For installing deep scrapers or flights.
With Centered Bushing	CB		Bars penetrating a chain to be installed.
With WS	WS		For prevention of conveyed materials leakage.
With Extended Pin	EP1 EP2 EP3		A hollow pipe or something to be installed on edge of the pin.
With Stay-Pin	TN		Material to be put directly on stay-pins or wire mesh laced around pins.
With KY	KY1 KY2		For storage of cyclindrical materials.

There are two types depending on open and closed position of the attachment.

Type 1

Type 2

230

Table 6.7 Plus α Alpha Attachments

With Top Plate	TP1 TP2		Not to damage conveyed materials.
With Trolley Roller	TRO		For long-distance and horizontal conveying.
Resists Stick Slip	RFL		For smooth conveying without stick slipping.
With Outboard Roller	OR1 OR2 OR3		For supporting heavy loads.
With Stud Bushings	RFB		For longer wear life of bushing.
With Center Roller	CRR CRF		For easy replacement of roller when it is worn.
With Guide Shoe	GSA GSK		For prevention of chain's winding travel.
With Guide Roller	GR		For horizontal conveying.
With Solid Pusher	KD1 KD2		To push materials with the pusher.

KD1: Dog not attached to plate.
KD2: Dog attached to plate.

Table Surface
Direction of Travel

With Dog Roller	RD		To convey cylindrical materials by pushing.

When cylindrical materials are conveyed, material surface is not damaged, and rotating friction is reduced by using this attachment.

Table Surface

Applications

Table 6.8 Plus α Alpha Attachments

With Tilting Dog	CD		For storage of materials on the table surface.
When material on the conveyor runs relatively faster than the chain, the dog is pushed down from behind to enable material to pass over. The dog then resumes its original position.			
With Roller Tilting Dog	RCD		For storage of cylindrical materials.
When the conveyor runs on descent, the dog prevents the cylindrical material from excessive run. When the material is in front of the dog, the dog is pushed down and can store the material.			
With Ducking Dog	DD		For leaving materials at the designated station.
The dog is supported on the guide rail to convey material. When the guide rail is interrupted, the dog ducks down, leaves the material, and passes beneath it.			
With Teeth Dog	TD		For storage of cylindrical materials without noise.
The dog functions best when the chain conveys the material on descent, preventing it from excessive run and storing it. As the dog resumes its original position at the engagement of a sprocket tooth, it does not damage the material and makes little noise.			
With ID	ID		For both storage and pushing.
At the time that the dog pushes the material, if unexpected load operates the dog, it ducks down, leaving the material as it passes beneath it.			

6.6 SPECIAL ATTACHMENTS

Special attachments are designed for specific applications and are used infrequently. In Applications Section 2.5, we discussed who should make special attachment—the chain manufacturer or the user. Please refer to the section for details.

For large pitch conveyor chain, the tolerance of the height of a ground A or K attachment from the guide rail to the upper side of the "Precision Ground" attachment is ± 0.4 mm. This value is larger than the tolerance for RS conveyor chains.

Figure 6.41 shows examples of special attachments.

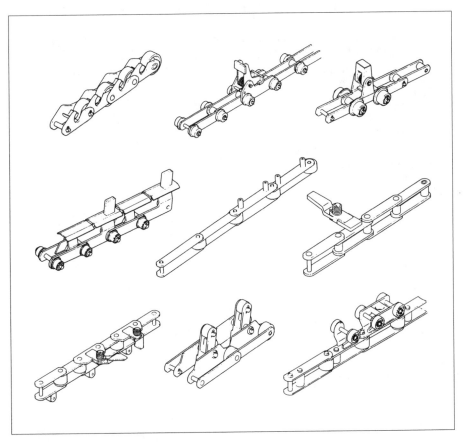

Figure 6.41   Examples of Special Attachments

BIBLIOGRAPHY

1. Atsushi Okoshi, *Roller Chain*, Korona-sha, Japan (1960).
2. Masataka Nakakomi, *Safety Design of Roller Chain*, Yoken-do, Japan (1989).
3. Shizuo Aoi, *Chain Conveyor*, Yakumo-shoten, Japan (1958).
4. Utaro Majima, *Chain-Conveyor*, Kogaku Tosho, Japan (1967).
5. R. C. Binder, *Mechanics of the Roller Chain Drive*, Prentice-Hall, Inc., NJ (1956).
6. L. Jones (Ed.), *Mechanical Handling with Precision Conveyor Chain*, Hutchinson & Co., London (1971).
7. L. L. Faulkner, S. B. Menkes (Ed.), *Chains for Power Transmission and Material Handling*, Marcel Dekker (1982).
8. Hans-Guenter Rachner, *Stahlgelenkketten und Kettentriebe*, Springer-Verlag, Berlin (1962).
9. Catalog, Tsubakimoto Chain Co.
10. Catalog, Daido Kogyo.
11. Catalog, Izumi Chain.
12. Catalog, Borg-Warner Automotive.
13. Catalog, Rexnord.
14. Catalog, Renold.

Coffee Break

The Tools Developed from Chain
Here we show three unique tools developed from chains.

1. Tough Roller (Figure 1)
This tool consists of a frame and an endless assembly of rollers wrapping around a center plate in the frame.

Comparing Tough Roller design to general roller bearing, the center plate in the frame works as an inner ring, and the surface on which the Tough Roller travels acts as an outer ring. Rollers function like cylindrical roller bearings, and the plate, together with the pin, act as a retainer. Due to its features, like high capacity (maximum allowable load = 100 tons) for its small body size, small running friction and low center of gravity, this tool is used in low-frequency conveyance of heavy objects.

2. Shafted Bearing Roller (Figure 2)
In this bearing roller, the roller has a shaft installed on it, which permits use as a support or guide wheel.

There are a variety of sizes and options available in this construction. Roller diameters range from 31.8 to 125 mm; maximum allowable load from 1.27 to 27.5 kN. The roller can be an R-type or F-type. There are various options, such as a urethane coating applied to the outer surface, or there can be a 5-degree taper in the channel.

3. Attachment with Shafted Bearing Roller
In this bearing roller, the roller is attached to the K-1 attachment of the chain. It can be used as support or a guiding wheel. Capacity and specifications are the same as for the shafted bearing roller.

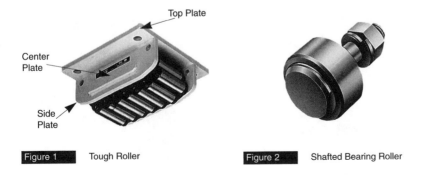

Top Plate

Center
Plate

Side
Plate

Figure 1   Tough Roller

Figure 2   Shafted Bearing Roller

Coffee Break

Sizing Up Chain

1. Teeny Tiny

The smallest standard transmission chain is Number 25. The chain pitch is 6.35 mm and minimum tensile strength is 3.50 kN. The smallest chain currently manufactured, although it is not standard, is Number 10, which is used in office equipment. It has a pitch of 3.175 mm and minimum tensile strength of 0.98 kN. There are a lot of micromachines (less than 1 mm) being made, but the chain to fit them is not currently available.

2. Stupendous

The largest standard transmission chain is Number 240, which has a pitch of 76.2 mm and average tensile strength of 500.4 kN. There are larger chains, but they are not standard. A Number 400, for example, has a pitch of 127 mm and average tensile strength of 1,730 kN. Multistrand versions of this chain are available, as well, from some manufacturers. Their tensile strengths are the multiplication of a single strand. Check with your manufacturer for availability.

The largest chain ever used had a pitch of 1,400 mm. It was created for horizontal rotating parking equipment.

The highest average tensile strength for a single chain—900 tonf—was a block chain. It was used in the production of steel tubing. If this chain were to be used in a multistrand configuration, its average tensile strength would be multiplied.

However, considering the cost, tensile strength of 500 tonf is the limit for a single roller chain.

Coffee Break

Speed Variation

Chains are usually used at low speeds with large loads. Some common chain types and speeds include the following:

> Transmission roller chain: less than 150 m/min.
> Small pitch conveyor chain: 10 to 30 m/min.
> Precision conveyor chain: less than 50 m/min.
> Top chain: 10 to 30 m/min.
> Free flow chain: 5 to 10 m/min.
> Large pitch conveyor chain: 10 to 30 m/min.

There are chains that are designed for high-speed operations. Here are some examples:

- The chain used in balancer drives in automotive engines can run at 1,800 m/min., which is the same speed as a cog belt. Chain pitch is less than 8 mm.
- Chain that drives the rear wheels of racing motorcycles operates at 1,500 m/min.
- The chain for the camshaft drives in marine diesel engines operates at about 600 m/min. Chain pitch is greater than 100 mm.
- The top chain that moves beer cans in breweries runs at 200 m/min.
- Large pitch conveyor chains and block chains in steel processing plants can run at speeds of 330 m/min. The chain pitch is 150 mm.

In each of these high-speed operations, the chain must be selected carefully. It's important to consider not only the strength and wear resistance, but the type of lubrication required. When you set up a high-speed chain system, make sure you work with a reliable supplier, and ask to see some actual performance results for the chain you are considering.

AFTERWORD

For designers and users of equipment, the most important points to consider for power transmission and conveyor operations are how well they stand up to and satisfy the following:

Power Transmission Operations
1. Quality: The features of the transmitted power, maintenance, length of working life.
2. Cost: Initial cost, running cost.
3. Delivery: Availability.

Conveyor Operations
1. Quality: Speed, accuracy, flexibility, maintenance, length of working life.
2. Cost: Initial cost, running cost.
3. Delivery: Availability.

Of course, these points can be applied to much more than just chain. You also have to compare belts, gears, and even other tools.

Power transmission and conveyors are rarely treated scientifically. At colleges and universities, chains are often ignored in lectures about technology. Many people think that chain is simply an old machine element.

But chain is more than that. Used correctly, chain can have a major impact on the entire operation. Here's an example: By replacing steel rollers with engineered plastic rollers on conveyor chains and moving from plastic rollers to bearing rollers, the coefficient of friction was reduced to one-fourth or one-fifth of the original. This results in lower costs for driving parts and frames, and saves energy. Progress in chains has a direct connection to economizing energy.

I have worked with many customers in many different fields during my career. I noticed that there was no handbook to explain the different types of chains, nor a book that describes the ease and convenience of using chain.

This book is designed to solve these problems. First, I explained the main ideas about chain. Then, I picked 50 types of chain in current use and gave practical points—application examples, construction and features, sprockets, selection and handling, technical trends—so that readers can work the chain's ability fully into their equipment. There is no denying the fact that most of the chain names and types are products of Tsubaki. Although other manufacturers also produce most of the chain types shown in this book, the lack of materials and the wide variation in products make comparisons very difficult.

I wish to express my sincere thanks to Mr. Toshiharu Yamamoto, the late Mr. Katsumi Kotegawa, and other senior experts who developed the company's technology, Mr. Keichi Sawata, Mr. Sumio Watanabe, Mr. Shinobu Takeda, Mr. Susumu Saijo (who provided good materials), and Mr. Tadahisa Yoshida for valuable advice.

May 1995
Makoto Kanehira